# Basic Knowledge Revised Higher Physics

*by*

## Dr. J.L. Page

ISBN 0 7169 3170 2

ROBERT GIBSON · Publisher
17 Fitzroy Place, Glasgow, G3 7SF.

# INTRODUCTION

This book is intended as a revision aid for candidates attempting the Revised Higher Physics Examination of the Scottish Examination Board. It is expected that you, the reader, will use other sources on experiments, applications and examples.

Note that the examination is designed to allow candidates to demonstrate **Knowledge and Understanding** and **Problem Solving** abilities. This book covers all the knowledge and understanding learning outcomes and also includes material which should prove useful for problem solving.

There are many ways of linking the topics covered in the course. However, to avoid confusion with other lists of learning outcomes you might be using, this book generally follows the order of the learning outcomes issued by the Scottish Examination Board. The three units of the course are each covered in a separate chapter. Remember there is no choice of question in either of the examination papers.

Each chapter begins with a checklist of what you are expected to be able to do in each unit, along with a list of physical quantities and formulae. This is followed by a concise treatment of the main topics of the unit.

The book can be used in several ways as part of an active revision programme. One approach would be

1. Read the checklist and write down what you know about each item.

2. Try to reproduce the formulae list.

3. Write down all the formulae which involve a certain quantity, e.g. force or energy.

This gives an awareness that the same formulae may be applied in different units.

Remember that although Physics is not simply about formulae and definitions understanding often comes by studying these. Try to visualise a situation to which a particular relationship applies or a problem you have solved using the relationship.

# CONTENTS

# Chapter 1

## MECHANICS AND PROPERTIES OF MATTER

### 1.1 CHECKLIST

**Kinematics**

You should be able to

- [ ] 1. define and list scalar and vector quantities;
- [ ] 2. use a scale diagram or calculation to find the resultant of several displacements or velocities;
- [ ] 3. resolve a vector into two components at right angles to each other;
- [ ] 4. define and calculate acceleration from numerical or graphical data;
- [ ] 5. describe a method of measuring acceleration;
- [ ] 6. show how the following equations of motion can be derived
  (1) $v = u + at$
  (2) $s = ut + \frac{1}{2}at^2$
  (3) $v^2 = u^2 + 2as$;
- [ ] 7. solve problems using the equations of motion;
- [ ] 8. suggest from information on graphs or numerical data whether an object is moving with *(a)* constant speed, *(b)* constant acceleration or *(c)* varying acceleration;
- [ ] 9. interpret displacement-time, velocity-time and acceleration-time graphs;
- [ ] 10. draw a velocity-time graph from a displacement-time graph;
- [ ] 11. draw an acceleration-time graph from a velocity-time graph;
- [ ] 12. solve problems involving projectile motion;
- [ ] 13. use the following terms correctly — distance, displacement, speed, constant or uniform speed, average speed, constant or uniform velocity, acceleration.

4

## Dynamics

You should be able to

☐ 1. define the unit of force, the newton;

☐ 2. solve problems using $F = ma$;

☐ 3. analyse the forces on an object by the use of a free body diagram;

☐ 4. find the resultant of several forces by scale diagram or graphical method;

☐ 5. resolve a force into two perpendicular components;

☐ 6. solve problems involving resolution of forces or vector addition of forces;

☐ 7. define momentum as the product of mass and velocity;

☐ 8. state the law of conservation of linear momentum;

☐ 9. distinguish between elastic and inelastic collisions;

☐ 10. solve problems using the law of conservation of momentum;

☐ 11. for the interaction of two objects moving in one dimension use the law of conservation of momentum to show that
    (i) the changes in momentum of each object are equal in size and opposite in sense
    (ii) the force acting on each object during the interaction are equal in size and opposite in sense;

☐ 12. state that impulse = force × time;

☐ 13. state that impulse = change in momentum;

☐ 14. solve problems involving impulse = change in momentum;

☐ 15. solve problems involving the interchange of potential and kinetic energy;

☐ 16. describe an experiment in which kinetic energy and potential energy are interchanged and measured;

☐ 17. use the following terms correctly — force, resultant force, horizontal and vertical component, resolution, momentum, impulse, elastic, inelastic.

5

**Properties of Matter**

You should be able to

☐ 1. state that pressure is the force per unit area and has the unit pascal or newton per square metre;

☐ 2. solve problems involving pressure, force and area;

☐ 3. state that density is mass per unit volume;

☐ 4. solve problems involving density, mass and volume;

☐ 5. describe an experiment to measure the density of air;

☐ 6. state that when a substance changes from the solid or liquid state to the gaseous state
  (i) its volume increases by a factor of $10^3$,
  (ii) its density decreases by a factor of $10^{-3}$;

☐ 7. describe an experiment to verify the statement in (6);

☐ 8. state that the pressure in a liquid is directly proportional to depth in the liquid and to the density of the liquid;

☐ 9. explain buoyancy force and flotation in terms of the forces acting on a body in a liquid;

☐ 10. describe the kinetic model of a gas and how it accounts for the pressure of a gas;

☐ 11. state that the pressure of a fixed mass of gas is inversely proportional to its volume provided the temperature remains constant;

☐ 12. describe an experiment to verify the relationship in (11);

☐ 13. change temperature in °C to kelvin and vice-versa;

☐ 14. state that the pressure of a fixed mass of gas is directly proportional to its temperature in kelvin;

☐ 15. describe an experiment to verify the relationship in (14);

☐ 16. solve problems involving the relationships in (11) and (14);

☐ 17. describe how the kinetic model predicts qualitatively the pressure/volume and pressure/temperature laws;

☐ 18. use the following terms correctly — density, pressure, buoyancy force, flotation.

## 1.2 PHYSICAL QUANTITIES

| Quantity | Quantity Symbol | Unit Symbol Unit | Scalar/ Vector |
|---|---|---|---|
| **Dynamics** | | | |
| distance along path | $s$ | m metre | scalar |
| displacement | $s$ | m metre | vector |
| time | $t$ | s second | scalar |
| speed | $u, v$ | m s$^{-1}$ metre per second | scalar |
| velocity | $u, v$ | m s$^{-1}$ metre per second | vector |
| acceleration linear | $a$ | m s$^{-2}$ metre per second squared | vector |
| acceleration gravitational | $g$ | m s$^{-2}$ metre per second squared | vector |
| mass | $m$ | kg kilogram | scalar |
| force | $F$ | N newton | vector |
| weight | $W$ | N newton | vector |
| gravitational field strength | $g$ | N kg$^{-1}$ newton per kilogram | vector |
| momentum linear | $p$ | kg m s$^{-1}$ kilogram metre per second | vector |
| impulse | $p$ | Ns newton second | vector |
| energy kinetic | $E_k$ | J joule | scalar |
| energy potential | $E_p$ | J joule | scalar |
| work | $W, E$ | J joule | scalar |
| power | $P$ | W watt | scalar |
| **Properties of Matter** | | | |
| pressure | $p$ | Pa pascal | scalar |
| area | $A$ | m$^2$ square metre | scalar |
| volume | $V$ | m$^3$ cubic metre | scalar |

| Quantity | Quantity Symbol | Unit Symbol Unit | Scalar/ Vector |
|----------|-----------------|-------------------|----------------|
| density | $\rho$ | $kg\ m^{-3}$ kilogram per metre cubed | scalar |
| temperature | $T$ | K kelvin | scalar |

## 1.3 FORMULAE

1. Average speed $= \dfrac{\text{total distance travelled}}{\text{total time taken}}$ $\qquad \bar{v} = \dfrac{d}{t}$

2. Average velocity $= \dfrac{\text{displacement}}{\text{total time taken}}$ $\qquad \bar{v} = \dfrac{\Delta s}{\Delta t}$

3. Acceleration $= \dfrac{\text{change in velocity}}{\text{time for change}}$ $\qquad a = \dfrac{\Delta v}{\Delta t}$

   $\qquad\qquad\quad = \dfrac{v-u}{t}$

4. For constant acceleration: average speed $= \dfrac{u+v}{2}$

5. $v = u + at$

6. $s = ut + \frac{1}{2}at^2$

7. $v^2 = u^2 + 2as$

8. Unbalanced Force $F = ma$

9. Weight = mass × gravitational field strength $\quad W = mg$

10. Momentum (linear) = mass × velocity $\quad p = mv$

11. Work = force × distance moved $\quad W = Fs$

12. Power $= \dfrac{\text{work done}}{\text{time taken}}$ $\quad P = \dfrac{W}{t}$

13. Kinetic Energy $= E_k = \frac{1}{2}mv^2$

14. Potential Energy $= E_p = mgh$

15. Impulse on object = force × time during which force acts on object
    $$p = Ft$$

16. Impulse on object = change in momentum of object
    $$p = \Delta(mv) = mv - mu$$

17. Unbalanced force $= \dfrac{\text{change in momentum}}{\text{time for change}}$ $\qquad F = \dfrac{mv - mu}{t}$

18. Pressure $p = \dfrac{F}{A}$

19. Density $\rho = \dfrac{m}{V}$

20. $p_1 V_1 = p_2 V_2$

21. $\dfrac{p_1}{T_1} = \dfrac{p_2}{T_2}$

22. $p \propto \rho h$ or $p = \rho g h$

## 1.4 KINEMATICS

### 1.4.1 Distance and Displacement

What is the difference between a **scalar** and a **vector** quantity? Simple! A scalar quantity needs only a **size** (with appropriate unit) to specify it whereas for a vector quantity you need to give a **compass direction** as well as a size. Temperature is obviously a scalar as it would be nonsense to say 10° due North! When you use physical quantities for the first time try to remember their definitions and decide whether the quantity is a scalar or a vector.

**Distance**, a scalar, requires only a **size** or **magnitude** to define it. Distances along a path of travel of an object are added **arithmetically** to obtain the total distance moved by the object.

**Displacement**, a vector, requires a **size** and **direction** to describe it fully. The resultant displacement for a journey is found by **vector addition** of the parts of the journey: problems may be solved by scale drawing or mathematically.

*Example 1.1*

A girl runs 300 m due East then 400 m due North. What is *(a)* the total distance travelled and *(b)* her resultant displacement from the starting point?

Solution:

Figure 1.1

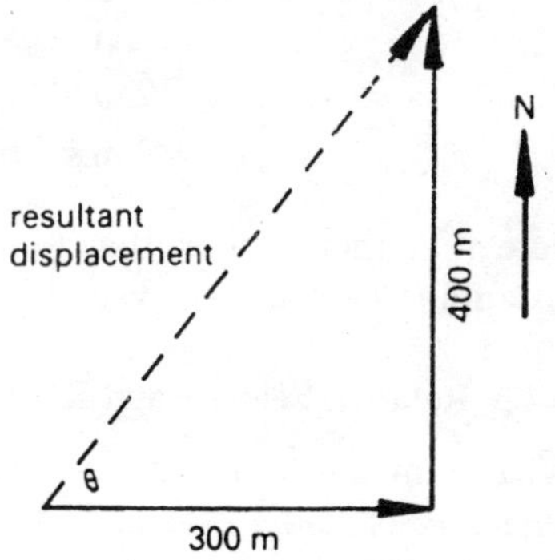

resultant displacement

N

400 m

θ

300 m

*(a)*  total distance = 300 + 400 = 700 m

*(b)*  by scale drawing

size of resultant displacement = 500 m
direction of resultant displacement = 53·1° N of E
OR
size of resultant displacement = $\sqrt{(300)^2 + (400)^2}$ m
the direction of the resultant displacement is given by the angle θ
where $\tan \theta = \dfrac{400}{300}$ giving θ = 53·1° N of E or a bearing of 036·9°.

9

### 1.4.2 Speed and Velocity

**Speed** is the rate of change of distance with time. Since distance and time are scalars then speed must be a scalar!

**Velocity** is the rate of change of displacement with time. Since displacement is a vector then velocity must also be a vector.

**Instantaneous** speeds and velocities are measurements of speed and velocity over **small time intervals** at fixed times.

*Example 1.2*

A girl jogs 300 m due East in 100 s then 400 m due North in 150 s. What is *(a)* her average speed and *(b)* her average velocity?

Solution: Use the diagram and solutions from the previous example then

*(a)* Average speed $= \dfrac{\text{total distance travelled}}{\text{total time taken}}$

$\qquad\qquad = \dfrac{700}{250} \text{ m s}^{-1}$

$\qquad\qquad = 2 \cdot 8 \text{ m s}^{-1}$

*(b)* Average velocity $= \dfrac{\text{total displacement}}{\text{total time taken}}$

$\qquad\qquad = \dfrac{500}{250} \text{ m s}^{-1} \text{ bearing } 036 \cdot 9°$

$\qquad\qquad = 2 \text{ m s}^{-1} \text{ bearing } 036 \cdot 9°$

**Note** that there is insufficient information given in the example to allow instantaneous speeds or velocities to be calculated.

### 1.4.3 Relative Velocity and Resultant Velocity

What is meant by relative velocity and how can it be illustrated? Well if an object A is said to be moving **relative to object B** then object B is being considered to be **at rest**. In a vector diagram this is shown by making the tail of the velocity vector the object B and the tip of the vector the object A.

Figure 1.2

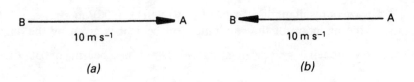

Figure 1.2 *(a)* represents A moving with a velocity of 10 m s$^{-1}$ due East **relative to B**. Figure 1.2 *(b)* represents B with a velocity of 10 m s$^{-1}$ due West **relative to A**. These figures illustrate exactly the same situations but viewed from a different reference point!

An object may have a velocity resulting from several causes. For example, the **resultant velocity** of an aircraft is caused by

*(a)* the aircraft engines moving it relative to the air

*(b)* the wind, whose velocity is usually given relative to the ground.

Now a simple example where the velocities are along a straight line, i.e. collinear.

*Example 1.3*

The engine of a model plane gives the plane a speed of 20 m s$^{-1}$ in still air. The plane is directed to fly due East into a wind which has velocity of 4 m s$^{-1}$ due West. What is the velocity of the plane relative to the ground?

Solution: Mathematically this involves adding **vectorially** the velocity caused by the engine to the velocity caused by the wind. First we draw the vectors as in Figure 1.3*(a)*

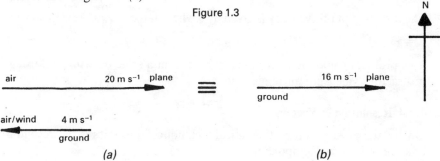

Figure 1.3

*(a)*                                                              *(b)*

Figure 1.3*(b)* shows that when the two vectors are added the resultant velocity of the plane is 16 m s$^{-1}$ due East.

Note that the two vectors in *(a)* have been drawn to scale and in such a way that the "air" which is common to both vectors is at the tip of one vector and the tail of the other.

As you know, in most situations velocities are not collinear. The next example shows how to deal with this type of problem.

*Example 1.4*

The engine of a model plane gives the plane a speed of 20 m s$^{-1}$ in still air. The plane is flying due East when it is hit by a gust of wind which has a velocity of 15 m s$^{-1}$ due North. Calculate the resultant velocity of the plane relative to the ground.

11

Solution:   Again the vectors are drawn to scale and combined "tip to tail" in such a way that the common word "air" is at the meeting point of the two vectors.

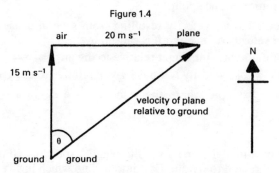

Figure 1.4

The magnitude of the velocity of the plane relative to ground
$$= \sqrt{(15)^2 + (20)^2}$$
$$= 25 \text{ m s}^{-1}$$

The direction of this velocity is given by $\theta$ where $\tan \theta = \dfrac{20}{15} = 1{\cdot}33$ giving $\theta = 53°$.

This problem could also have been solved from a scale drawing and using a protractor to measure the angle.

### 1.4.4 Resolution of Vectors

One of the most useful mathematical techniques in Physics is the resolution of a vector into two components.

In the special case any vector can be **resolved** into two **components** at right angles to each other. These two components together have the same result as the initial single vector.

How do you find the components of a vector which are at right angles to each other? This requires only very basic mathematics.

Figure 1.5

Since $\qquad \dfrac{v_x}{v} = \cos\theta \Rightarrow v_x = v\cos\theta$

$$\dfrac{v_y}{v} = \sin\theta \Rightarrow v_y = v\sin\theta$$

The $x$ and $y$ directions are chosen to suit the particular problem being solved.

Note that the technique of resolution is simply the converse of vector addition with the restriction of the components being at right angles to each other. The example below will show you how this technique can be used.

*Example 1.5*

Figure 1.6

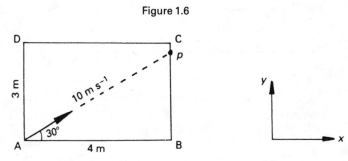

A puck is fired with a constant velocity of 10 m s⁻¹ across a frictionless surface as shown in figure 1.6. Calculate the time for the puck to reach edge BC.

Solution:    Resolve the initial velocity into a component along the $x$-axis and a component along the $y$-axis.

$v_x = 10\cos 30° = 8\cdot 7$ m s⁻¹

Time $t$ to travel $4\cdot 0$ m in the $x$-direction is

$$t = \dfrac{4}{8\cdot 7} = 0\cdot 46\ \text{s}$$

### 1.4.5   Acceleration

Suppose you find it difficult to think of acceleration as being a vector. Then first consider the definition: **Acceleration is the rate of change of velocity**.

If you are still not convinced then consider that to cause an object to accelerate you must apply an unbalanced force. Since the direction of the force will determine the direction of the acceleration of the object, then acceleration like force, must be a vector.

13

Acceleration $\quad a = \dfrac{v - u}{t}$

where $u$ is the initial velocity, $v$ is the final velocity and $t$ is the time for the change in velocity.

As change in velocity is a vector then an acceleration can be observed as a change in the magnitude **and/or** the direction of the velocity of an object.

Figure 1.7

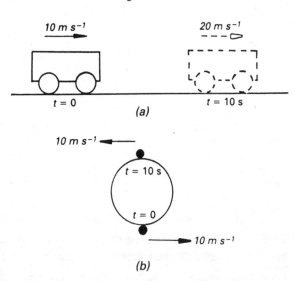

Figure 1.7 *(a)* illustrates a situation involving a trolley accelerating with **a change in speed only**: Figure 1.7 *(b)* shows a sphere travelling at constant speed and **only the direction of motion changes**. This last concept is clarified by observing that an unbalanced force is required to produce this acceleration. This force must be directed towards the centre of the circle.

If the movement of the object is in a straight line then calculation of the acceleration is simple.

*Example 1.6*

A ball, travelling with a velocity of 20 m s$^{-1}$, strikes a wall at right angles so that it rebounds back along the same path with a velocity of 16 m s$^{-1}$. If the time of impact of the ball with the wall is 0·2 s what is the average acceleration of the ball?

14

Solution:  We shall take vectors to the right to be positive and to
negative.

Figure 1.8

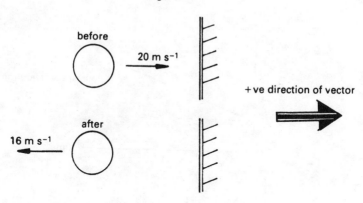

change in velocity $= v - u$
$$= (-16) - (+20)$$
$$= -36 \text{ m s}^{-1} \text{ or } 36 \text{ m s}^{-1} \text{ to the left.}$$

$\Rightarrow$     acceleration $= \dfrac{-36}{0\cdot2} \text{ m s}^{-2}$
$$= -180 \text{ m s}^{-2}$$

$\Rightarrow$ average acceleration is 180 m s$^{-2}$ to the left.

Note how important it is to use the correct signs for the directions of the
vectors.


### 1.4.6  Equations of Motion

These are among the most useful equations you will meet in Higher Physics.

Consider an object moving with the following conditions

$u$ = initial velocity

$v$ = final velocity after time $t$

$a$ = <u>constant</u> acceleration (in a straight line) during time $t$

$s$ = displacement (in a straight line) during time $t$

esented by these conditions is illustrated by the graph in

Figure 1.9

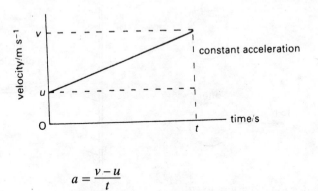

$$a = \frac{v - u}{t}$$

$$\Rightarrow \boxed{v = u + at}$$

The displacement in time $t$ is given by the area under the velocity-time graph.

$$s = ut + \tfrac{1}{2}t(v - u) \qquad \left[\text{since } \frac{v - u}{t} = a\right]$$

$$= ut + \tfrac{1}{2}t.at$$

$$\Rightarrow \boxed{s = ut + \tfrac{1}{2}at^2}$$

Using $\quad v = u + at$

$$\Rightarrow v^2 = (u + at)^2$$

$$= u^2 + 2uat + a^2t^2$$

$$= u^2 + 2a(ut + \tfrac{1}{2}at^2)$$

$$\Rightarrow \boxed{v^2 = u^2 + 2as}$$

The three boxed relationships are the equations of motion for an object travelling in a straight line with a **constant** acceleration.

When solving problems using these relationships you must assign positive and negative directions to the vector quantities. It is usual to adopt a Cartesian system as in figure 1.10

Figure 1.10

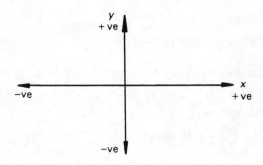

You can use these relationships whenever you have information about the movement of an object having **constant** acceleration.

*Example 1.7*

A ball is thrown vertically upwards from the surface of the earth with a velocity of 30 m s$^{-1}$. Calculate *(a)* the time for the ball to reach maximum height *(b)* the maximum height reached and *(c)* the time at which the displacement of the ball is 25 m. Assume that there is no air friction.

Solution:

Figure 1.11

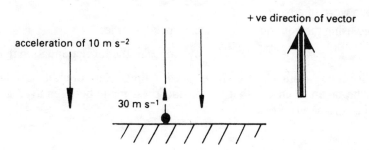

You might at first think there is insufficient data to solve this problem. Have you noticed that the assumption of no air friction implies that the only acceleration is caused by gravity?

**We shall assume that g at the earth's surface is 10 m s$^{-2}$.**

17

(a) What is given in the statement of the problem?

$$u = +30 \text{ m s}^{-1} \qquad a = -10 \text{ m s}^{-2} \qquad v = 0$$

Using $v = u + at$

$\Rightarrow \qquad 0 = 30 + (-10)t$

$\Rightarrow \qquad t = 3$

Time to reach maximum height is 3 s.

(b) Which quantities are now known for this part of the problem?

$$u = +30 \text{ m s}^{-1} \qquad a = -10 \text{ m s}^{-2} \qquad t = 3 \text{ s} \qquad v = 0$$

Using $v^2 = u^2 + 2as$

$\Rightarrow \qquad 0 = (30)^2 + 2(-10) \text{ s}$

$\Rightarrow \qquad s = 45$

Maximum height is 45 m

(c) Given quantities are $u = +30 \text{ m s}^{-1} \qquad a = -10 \text{ m s}^{-2} \qquad s = +25 \text{ m}$

Using $s = ut + \frac{1}{2}at^2 \Rightarrow +25 = (+30)t + \frac{1}{2}(-10)t^2$

$\Rightarrow \qquad t^2 - 6t + 5 = 0 \Rightarrow (t-1)(t-5) = 0$

This equation gives two possible values for $t$!

The ball therefore has a displacement of 25 m, on the way up, after 1 s and after 5 s when it is on the way down again.

**Note**: a word of advice.

Avoid using the equation    distance = speed × time.

Always use $s = ut + \frac{1}{2}at^2$ which may reduce to the former equation if $a = 0$.

The formula    distance = average speed × time    can often be used but care must be taken to ensure that the distinction is made between average speed and instantaneous speed.

### 1.4.7 Graphs of Motion in a Straight Line

Can you interpret graphs of displacement-time, velocity-time and acceleration-time?

You should remember the following:

Gradient at a point on $s - t$ graph → instantaneous velocity
Gradient at a point on $v - t$ graph → acceleration
Area under $a - t$ graph → velocity
Area under $v - t$ graph → displacement

Let us start with a displacement-time graph and derive the distance-time and acceleration-time graphs.

*Example 1.8*

Figure 1.12

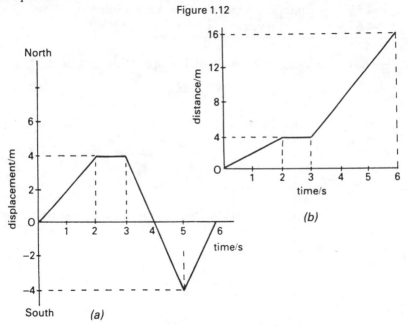

*(a)*

*(b)*

The object has moved from its starting position to a point 4 m due North after 2 s. It remains there for 1 s then changes its direction of movement to due South for a distance of 8 m, passing its starting position, to arrive 4 m due South of its starting point 5 s after the start. It now travels North for 1 s to arrive back at its starting position, i.e. a total displacement of 0 m.

Figure 1.12 *(b)* shows the distance-time graph obtained from the displacement-time graph.

19

Because a distance-time graph gives no information on direction it cannot be used to obtain a displacement-time graph.

Notes on the $s - t$ graph:

A constant gradient indicates a constant velocity.
A positive gradient represents a velocity North.
A negative gradient represents a velocity South.

For figure 1.12 this gives:

| Time interval | Velocity |
|---|---|
| $0\,s \rightarrow 2\,s$ | $+ 4/2 = 2$ m s$^{-1}$ North |
| $2\,s \rightarrow 3\,s$ | zero velocity |
| $3\,s \rightarrow 5\,s$ | constant velocity $= -8/2 = 4$ m s$^{-1}$ South |
| $5\,s \rightarrow 6\,s$ | constant velocity $= +4/2 = 4$ m s$^{-1}$ North |

This can be used to obtain the velocity-time graph shown in figure 1.13.

Figure 1.13

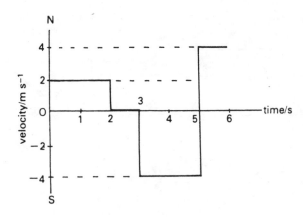

If the velocity-time graph had been the starting point for the problem then the displacement-time graph of figure 1.12 could be constructed from the **area** under the velocity-time graph as follows:

| Time | Displacement at this time | Distance up to this time |
|------|---------------------------|--------------------------|
| 1 s | 2 m | 2 m |
| 2 s | 4 m | 2 m + 2 m = 4 m |
| 3 s | 4 m + 0 = 4 m | 4 m + 0 m = 4 m |
| 4 s | 4 m – 4 m = 0 m | 4 m + 4 m = 8 m |
| 5 s | 0 – 4 m = –4 m | 8 m + 4 m = 12 m |
| 6 s | 4 m – 4 m = 0 m | 12 m + 4 m = 16 m |

In a similar way we can obtain an acceleration-time graph if the velocity-time graph of the motion is given. This is achieved by calculating the gradient of different sections of the velocity-time graph.

**Note:** when producing a speed-time graph from a velocity-time graph only the magnitudes of the velocity are retained.

A constant gradient on a $v - t$ graph indicates constant acceleration.
A positive gradient on a $v - t$ graph indicates acceleration North
A negative gradient on a $v - t$ graph indicates acceleration South.

The example below where the velocity-time graph is given in figure 1.14 illustrates the method. Note the similarity with the previous example!

*Example 1.9*

Figure 1.14

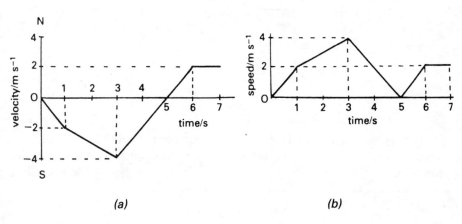

(a)                                           (b)

Graph *(a)* illustrates the motion of an object which starts from rest and moves due South with a constant acceleration for 1 s. After this time its acceleration decreases and it reaches a maximum velocity of 4 m s⁻¹ due South at 3 s. The velocity now decreases until after the 5th second it is travelling due North. After the 6th second its velocity remains fixed at 2 m s⁻¹ due North. The corresponding speed-time graph is shown in figure 1.14 *(b)*.

Calculation of the gradients during the time intervals when the acceleration (gradient of graph) is constant gives the table below.

| Time interval | Acceleration |
|---|---|
| 0 s – 1 s | – 2 m s⁻² or 2 m s⁻² due South |
| 1 s – 3 s | – 1 m s⁻² or 1 m s⁻² due South |
| 3 s – 6 s | +2 m s⁻² or 2 m s⁻² due North |
| 6 s – 7 s | 0 m s⁻² |

This data gives the graph of figure 1.15.

Figure 1.15

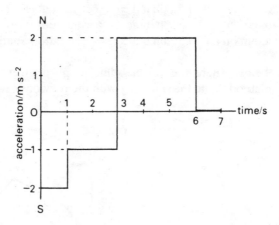

Note that the object may have a velocity due South while its acceleration is due North, e.g. at the 4th second. A common mistake is to take the displacement to be 0 at the 5th second on this type of graph. The displacement is really 11 m due South from the starting position.

## Graphs for Constant Speed

Figure 1.16

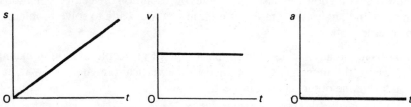

## Graphs for Constant Acceleration

Figure 1.17

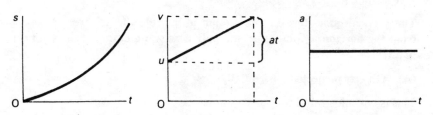

Did you notice that the three graphs of figure 1.17 are plots of the equations of motion for constant acceleration?

$$s = ut + \tfrac{1}{2}at^2 \quad \text{a parabola}$$
$$v = u + at \quad \text{a straight line}$$

## Graphs for Varying Acceleration

The simplest case of varying acceleration is when the acceleration is directly proportional to time. This is shown in figure 1.18 *(b)*. Since the acceleration is increasing with time the $v - t$ graph must show an increasing slope as $t$ increases as in *(a)*.

Figure 1.18

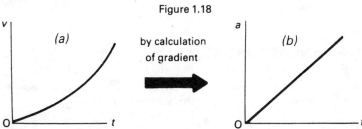

Given numerical values on one of the graphs you should be able to obtain the second graph by calculation of gradients or areas.

23

### 1.4.8 Projectiles

Now that you know the basic techniques of resolution of vectors, equations of motion and analysis of graphs of motion you are ready to solve problems on projectile motion.

You have already tackled the simplest type of projectile motion in example 1.7 where the movement is confined to the vertical direction. How then do you tackle the other types of projectile?

In many projectile problems the assumption is made that air resistance can be neglected. The only acceleration is then caused by the effect of gravity and this **always gives an acceleration towards the earth's surface**. There is **no acceleration in the horizontal direction.**

**The vertical quantities for the motion of a projectile are treated separately from the horizontal quantities: the only common quantity is the total time of flight.**

**(A)   Objects projected horizontally**

This is best illustrated with an example.

*Example 1.10*

A sphere is projected with a horizontal velocity of 20 m s$^{-1}$ over the edge of a cliff.

Figure 1.19

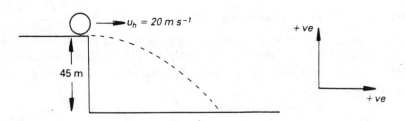

If the height of the cliff is 45 m and air resistance is neglected find *(a)* the time for the sphere to reach the ground, *(b)* the distance of the landing point from the base of the cliff and *(c)* the velocity of the sphere just before it hits the ground. Assume that $g$ at the earth's surface is 10 m s$^{-2}$

Solution:
Define upwards to be the positive direction for vertical vectors and to the right to be positive for horizontal vectors.

24

*(a)* What do you know from the statement of the problem?

| *vertical quantities* | *horizontal quantities* |
|---|---|
| $u_v = 0$ | $u_h = +20 \text{ m s}^{-1}$ |
| $a_v = -10 \text{ m s}^{-2}$ | $a_h = 0$ |
| $s_v = -45 \text{ m}$ | |

Note $s_v$ is the displacement after the time of flight $t$ and must be negative.

Then using the values of only the vertical components

$$s_v = u_v t + \tfrac{1}{2} a_v t^2$$
$$\Rightarrow -45 = 0t + \tfrac{1}{2}(-10)t^2$$
$$\Rightarrow 45 = 5t^2$$

$t^2 = 9 \Rightarrow t = \pm 3$. Two solutions! The solution relating to our problem is $t = +3$ giving a time of flight of 3 s.

*(b)* Using the values of only the horizontal components.

$$s_h = u_h t + \tfrac{1}{2} a_h t^2$$
$$= 20 \times 3 + \tfrac{1}{2} \times 0 \times (3)^2$$
$$= 60$$

The horizontal range from the foot of the cliff is 60 m.

*(c)* As there is **no horizontal acceleration** the horizontal component of the velocity remains constant at 20 m s$^{-1}$ until the sphere hits the ground.

To find the vertical component just before impact

$$v_v = u_v + a_v t$$
$$= 0 + (-10) \times 3$$
$$\Rightarrow v_v = -30 \text{ m s}^{-1}$$

Note the negative sign shows that the direction of the vertical component of velocity is downwards just before impact, as expected.

The horizontal and vertical components just before impact are combined as in figure 1.20 to find the resultant velocity.

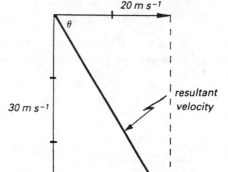

Figure 1.20

The size of the resultant velocity is $\sqrt{20^2 + 30^2} = 36 \text{ m s}^{-1}$. Its direction is given by $\tan \theta = \dfrac{30}{20} = 1 \cdot 5$ giving $\theta = 56°$ to the horizontal.

## (B) Objects projected upwards at an angle

With this type of projectile it is important to remember that **the initial velocity of the projectile must be resolved into its horizontal and vertical components.**

The following example illustrates the technique.

*Example 1.11*

A sphere is launched with an initial velocity of 20 m s$^{-1}$ at an angle of 30° to a horizontal surface. Find *(a)* its time of flight and *(b)* the maximum height reached by the sphere. Neglect air friction. Assume $g = 10$ m s$^{-2}$.

Solution:

Figure 1.21

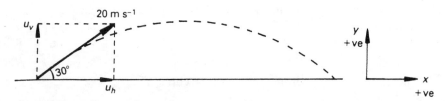

By resolving the initial velocity

Initial horizontal velocity $= u_h = 20 \cos 30° = 17{\cdot}3$ m s$^{-1}$

Initial vertical velocity $\quad = u_v = 20 \sin 30° = 10$ m s$^{-1}$

*(a)* We are given that $\quad s_v = 0 \qquad u_v = +10$ m s$^{-1}$ $\qquad a_v = -10$ m s$^{-2}$

Note $s_v = 0$ is the vertical displacement from the starting point after the time of flight $t$ for this part of the problem.

$$s_v = u_v + \tfrac{1}{2}a_v t^2$$
$$\Rightarrow \quad 0 = 10t + \tfrac{1}{2}(-10)t^2$$
$$\Rightarrow t^2 - 2t = 0$$
$$\Rightarrow t(t-2) = 0$$

giving $t = 0$ or 2.

Two solutions for this problem!

The time of flight is therefore 2 s. The solution $t = 0$ applies to the displacement being zero at the start of the problem but adds nothing new to the knowledge of the situation.

Note a solution could also have been found by calculating the time for the sphere to reach its maximum height (when $v_v = 0$) and doubling this value.

(b) $v_v = 0 \qquad u_v = +10 \text{ m s}^{-1} \qquad a_v = -10 \text{ m s}^{-2}$

$\qquad v^2{}_v = u^2{}_v + 2a_v s_v$

$\Rightarrow \quad 0 = (10)^2 + 2(-10)s_v$

$\Rightarrow \quad s_v = \dfrac{100}{20} = 5$

The maximum height is therefore 5 m.

It may be instructive to study the graphs shown in figure 1.22 of the horizontal and vertical components of displacement, velocity and acceleration for this projectile.

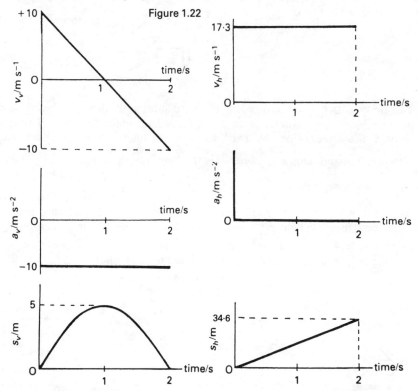

Figure 1.22

Starting from the velocity-time graphs the acceleration and displacement-time graphs can be obtained using the methods of 1.4.7.

27

### 1.4.9 Measurement of Speed and Acceleration

You should be able to describe methods of measuring speed and acceleration stating which quantities are measured in the method and how these are used to obtain values of speed and acceleration.

### (A) SPEED

A card of known length $l$ is attached to the moving object as in figure 1.23.

**Figure 1.23**

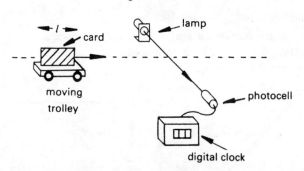

The timer starts to operate when the card interrupts the light beam to the photocell and stops when the card has passed through the beam. The timer records the time $t$ for the card to pass through the beam. The speed is then calculated from $v = \dfrac{l}{t}$ where $l$ is the length of the card.

### (B) ACCELERATION

Acceleration can be measured in several ways but the method which is easiest to understand uses two light gates and an interface attached to a microcomputer.

In figure 1.24 two light gates are placed so that the light beams will be interrupted by the passage of a card attached to the trolley.

**Figure 1.24**

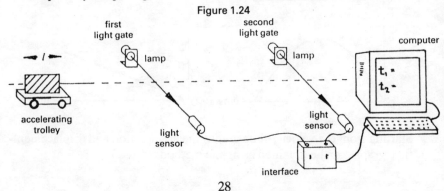

28

The software used by the microcomputer measures **three** time intervals. These are the time taken for the card to travel

*(a)* through the first light gate, $t_1$
*(b)* through the second light gate, $t_2$
*(c)* between the first and the second light gates, $t_3$.

Having been given the length of $l$ of the card the computer uses $t_1$ and $t_2$ to calculate the initial speed and the final speed of the trolley. The acceleration is then calculated using

acceleration = (final speed – initial speed)/$t_3$.

Note that the above method measures the **average** acceleration of the trolley between the two gates. To obtain a value close to the **instantaneous** acceleration the two gates should be placed as close together as possible.

## 1.5 DYNAMICS

### 1.5.1 Newton's First Law

This law states that "**A body will stay at rest or move with a constant velocity unless acted on by an unbalanced (resultant) force**".

An important implication in this statement is that no **unbalanced** force is required to keep an object moving with constant velocity when the object is in motion.

**Note:**

1. If an object changes speed in a straight line there must be an unbalanced force acting on it. Once this unbalanced force is removed the object travels with constant speed.

2. If an object is travelling in a circle with constant speed there must be an unbalanced force on it towards the centre of the circle. If this force is removed the object will travel in a tangent to the circle.

### 1.5.2 Newton's Second Law

This states that "**The rate of change of momentum of a body is equal to the unbalanced force acting on the body and takes place in the direction of this force**". This gives the relationship

$$F = \frac{\text{final momentum} - \text{initial momentum}}{\text{time for change in momentum}}$$

$$= \frac{mv - mu}{t}$$

Since $a = \frac{v-u}{t}$ and $F = \frac{m(v-u)}{t}$

then $F = ma$

**Note:**

1. $t$ is the time during which the unbalanced force acts to cause the change in momentum.

2. A change in momentum may also arise through a change in mass.

The equation $F = ma$ may be used to define the size of the unit of force, the Newton. An unbalanced force of 1 N is that force which when acting on a mass of 1 kg produces an acceleration of 1 m s$^{-2}$.

Two experimental arrangements to measure force in terms of mass and acceleration are shown in figure 1.25.

Figure 1.25

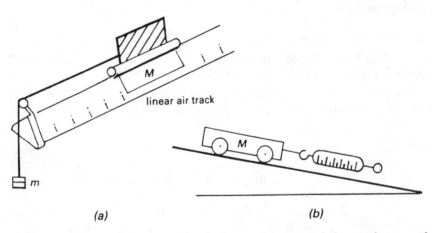

(a)                        (b)

In *(a)* the mass $m$ is kept small relative to the mass of the carriage on the linear air track. The unbalanced force $F$ causing the acceleration will be equal to $mg$. The resulting acceleration $a$ of the carriage can be measured using the light beam technique of section 1.4.9. Then if the pulley is friction free

$$F = mg = (M + m)a$$

The value of $F$ can then be compared with the product $(M + m)a$.

In *(b)* the trolley is placed on a friction compensated runway and its acceleration measured while a force $F$ is applied by means of the newton or spring balance.

The value of $F$ can be compared with the product $Ma$.

### 1.5.3   Problem Solving using $F = ma$

While it is not possible to give examples of all types of problems you might encounter some hints should prove useful.

PROCEDURE
1.  Draw a sketch of the problem situation.
2.  Draw a free-body diagram for the object whose motion is being analysed and indicate **all** the forces acting on **this** object.
3.  On the free-body diagram mark the direction of the acceleration of the object (or the unbalanced force on the object).
4.  Mark the positive direction of the vectors.
5.  Apply $F = ma$.

A good illustration of this type of problem is that involving lifts.

*Example 1.12*

An object of mass 5 kg is suspended from a spring balance fixed to the roof of a lift. If the reading on the spring balance is 70 N calculate the acceleration of the object (and hence of the lift).

Solution:

The situation is sketched in figure 1.26 and the steps carried out as in the procedure.

Figure 1.26

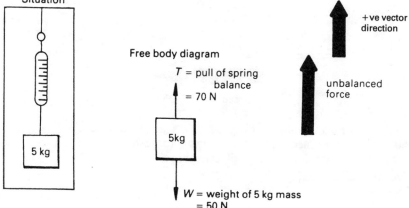

Once the forces have been drawn on the diagram it is clear that the unbalanced force and hence the acceleration are upwards.

Unbalanced force $F = 70 - 50$

$$\Rightarrow F = 20 \text{ N upwards}$$

Using
$$F = ma$$
$$\Rightarrow 20 = 5a$$
$$\Rightarrow a = 4 \text{ m s}^{-2} \text{ upwards}$$

The next type of problem is perhaps slightly more difficult but the techniques are still the same.

*Example 1.13*

A force of 125 N is used to pull two blocks, coupled by a string, on a horizontal surface as shown in figure 1.27.

Figure 1.27

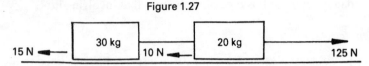

The force of friction is 15 N on the block of mass 30 kg and 10 N on the block of mass 20 kg. Calculate the tension in the string between the blocks.

Solution:

First consider the forces acting on the combined system of mass 50 kg as in figure 1.28 *(a)*.

Figure 1.28

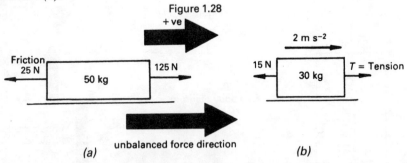

This gives an unbalanced force of 100 N acting on the combined mass of 50 kg to give an acceleration of 2 m s$^{-2}$ to both blocks. Then the block of mass 30 kg is considered by itself as in *(b)*.

Unbalanced force $F = ma$

$$\Rightarrow T + (-15) = 30 \times 2$$
$$\Rightarrow T = 75 \text{ N}$$

Tension in string is 75 N

32

### 1.5.4 Momentum

The concept of the momentum of an object leads to a powerful technique in the solution of problems in mechanics. But first what is momentum?

Momentum $p$ = mass × velocity = $mv$

Momentum is a vector with the unit kg m s⁻¹.

**The law of conservation of linear momentum states that "in the absence of external forces the total linear momentum of a system of interacting bodies remains constant".**

In problems, the velocities of objects **immediately** after a collision are calculated before any external forces such as friction have time to alter the velocities.

**Remember** since momentum is a vector a positive vector direction must be defined when solving problems.

*Example 1.14*

A trolley A of mass 2 kg with a velocity of 5 m s⁻¹ collides head on with a trolley B of mass 4 kg having a velocity of 3 m s⁻¹ in the opposite direction. The trolleys stick together on impact. Calculate their velocity immediately after the collision.

Figure 1.29

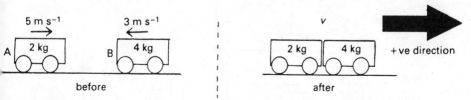

Solution:

Total momentum before collision    =    total momentum after collision

⇒ momentum of A + momentum of B = momentum of A + momentum of B
$\quad\quad$ before $\quad\quad\quad\quad$ before $\quad\quad\quad\quad$ after $\quad\quad\quad\quad$ after

$\Rightarrow 2 \times (+5) + 4 \times (-3) \quad\quad = 2v + 4v$

$\Rightarrow \quad\quad\quad -2 \quad\quad\quad\quad\quad = \quad\quad 6v$

$\Rightarrow \quad\quad\quad v \quad\quad\quad\quad\quad = \quad\quad -0.33$

The velocity after the collision is 0·33 m s⁻¹ to the left or in the direction of B before the collision took place.

33

B

## Types of Collision

In **all** collisions the total momentum is conserved (again if there are no external forces).

The **total** energy in **all** collisions is conserved: the sum of the kinetic energies before the collision will equal the sum of the kinetic energies plus any sound, heat, etc. produced.

If the kinetic energy is conserved the collision is said to be **elastic**. If the kinetic energy is **not** conserved the collision is **inelastic**.

## Momentum and Newton's Third Law

**Newton's Third Law states "if a body A exerts a force on body B then body B will exert a force of equal magnitude but opposite direction on A".**

Note that each of the pair of forces acts on a different object.

Figure 1.30

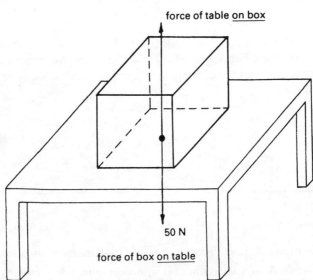

force of table on box

50 N

force of box on table

In figure 1.30 a box of mass 5 kg is placed on a table. The box exerts a force of 50 N (equal to its weight) downwards on the table. The table must therefore exert a force of 50 N upwards on the box (otherwise the box would fall through the table).

34

In the same situation if we consider one force to be the weight of the box (i.e. the pull of the Earth on the box) then the other force in the pair is the pull of the box on the Earth!

Newton's Third Law can be inferred from the law of conservation of momentum. Consider a collision between object A (mass $m_A$ and velocity $u_A$) and object B (mass $m_B$ and velocity $u_B$) such that the resulting velocities are $v_A$ and $v_B$.

By conservation of momentum

$$m_A u_A + m_B u_B = m_A v_A + m_B v_B$$
$$\Rightarrow -(m_A v_A - m_A u_A) = (m_B v_B - m_B u_B)$$
$$\Rightarrow -\Delta(mv)_A = +\Delta(mv)_B$$

The momentum change of A is equal in size but opposite in direction to the change in momentum of B.

Obviously the time of impact $\Delta t$, during which the objects will be in contact, must be the same for both objects.

$$\Rightarrow -\frac{\Delta(mv)_A}{\Delta t} = \frac{\Delta(mv)_B}{\Delta t}$$
$$\Rightarrow -F_A = +F_B$$

This is a mathematical statement of Newton's Third Law.

### 1.5.5. Impulse

For any object the change in its momentum will depend on the size of the unbalanced force $F$ acting on it and the time $t$ during which the force is applied. The product $F \times t$ is known as the impulse $p$.

$$F = ma = \frac{mv - mu}{t}$$

$\Rightarrow$ Impulse $p = Ft = mv - mu$

Usually during a collision the force is not constant. Such a situation is shown in figure 1.31 and the graph can be used to obtain the average value of the force during impulse.

Figure 1.31

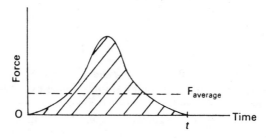

35

Area under $F-t$ graph = impulse

$$= \text{change in momentum}$$

An average impulse can be worked out from

$$p_{\text{average}} = \text{area under } F-t \text{ graph}$$

$$p_{\text{average}} = F_{\text{average}} t$$

$$\Rightarrow F_{\text{average}} = \frac{p_{\text{average}}}{t}$$

Now a problem to illustrate the theory.

*Example 1.15*

A ball of mass 2 kg is thrown with a speed of 20 m s$^{-1}$ such that it hits a wall at right angles to the surface. It rebounds along its original path with a speed of 20 m s$^{-1}$. If the time of impact is 0·02 s calculate the average force on the wall.

Figure 1.32

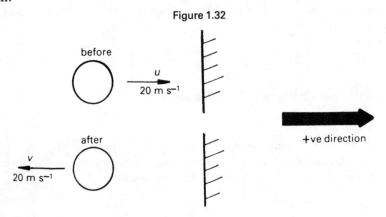

Solution:

change in momentum of ball $= mv - mu$

$$= 2 \times (-20) - 2 \times (20)$$

$$= -80 \text{ kg m s}^{-1}$$

Average force on the ball is given by

$$F_{\text{average}} t = \text{change in momentum of ball}$$

$$\Rightarrow F_{\text{average}} \times 0·02 = -80$$

$$\Rightarrow F_{\text{average}} = -4 \times 10^3$$

The average force on the **ball** (caused by the wall) is $4 \times 10^3$ N to the left or in the opposite direction to its original motion. Hence by Newton's Third Law: the average force on the **wall** (caused by the ball) is $4 \times 10^3$ N to the right or in the same direction as the original direction of the ball.

**Experimental Investigation of Average Force during Impulse**

Figure 1.33

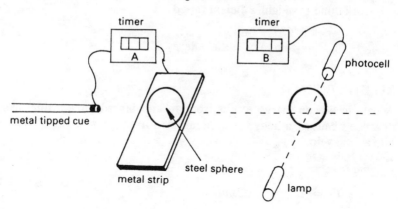

Figure 1.33 shows an experimental arrangement to investigate impulse.

Timer A records the time of impact $t_1$ between the metal tip of the cue and the metal sphere as it rolls over the strip of metal foil.

Timer B records the time of travel $t_2$ of the sphere through the photocell gate; thus allowing the speed of the sphere to be calculated from $v = d/t_2$ where $d$ is the diameter of the sphere.

As the sphere started from rest $F_{average} t_1 = mv$ where $m$ is the mass of the sphere. Hence $F_{average}$ can be calculated.

### 1.5.6  Work, Energy and Power

Work done is defined as the product of the force and the distance through which the force acts (if the force is constant over this distance).

$$W = F \text{ s}$$

The area under a force-distance graph will give the work done by the force.

### (A) POTENTIAL ENERGY

If a body of mass $m$ is raised through a height $h$, **at a constant speed**, then work is being done against the gravitational field. The work done is a measure of the energy being transformed into a gain in **potential energy**. Note the vertical force required to raise the body with **constant** speed must equal the weight of the body. If the vertical force applied is greater

37

than the weight of the object there will be an increase in kinetic energy as well as an increase in potential energy.

$$\text{work done} = \text{weight} \times \text{height raised}$$
$$= mgh$$
$$= \text{gain in potential energy}$$
$$= E_p$$

## (B) KINETIC ENERGY

A gain in **kinetic energy** results from an **unbalanced** force acting over a distance $s$ causing a body to accelerate uniformly from an initial velocity $u$ to a final velocity $v$.

$$F = ma = m\frac{v^2 - u^2}{2s} \qquad \text{since } v^2 = u^2 + 2as$$
$$Fs = 1/2\,mv^2 - 1/2\,mu^2$$

### Experiments on Energy Conversion

Figure 1.34 illustrates an experiment which can be used to investigate the conversion of potential energy into kinetic energy.

**Figure 1.34**

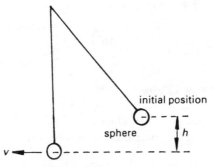

In the example the initial speed is zero and the final speed, after passing through a vertical height $h$, can be measured using a light beam and timer method. If the diameter $d$ of the sphere is measured the speed is calculated from $\frac{d}{t}$ where $t$ is the time during which the beam is cut off.

Since loss in $E_p$ = gain in $E_k$

$$\Rightarrow mgh = \tfrac{1}{2}mv^2$$
$$\Rightarrow \quad h = Av^2 \text{ where } A \text{ is constant}$$

A graph of $h$ against $v^2$ should be a straight line passing through the origin.

## Power

Power is the rate of doing work or the rate of energy transformation.

$$\text{Power } P = \frac{\text{work done}}{\text{time taken}} = \frac{W}{t}$$

If the work done by a **constant** force $F$ results in an object maintaining a **constant** speed $v$ over a distance $s$:

$$P = \frac{Fs}{t} = Fv$$

### 1.5.7 Addition and Resolution of Forces

**Vector Addition of Forces**

Forces acting on an object are added vectorially to give a resultant force whose effect is the same as the initial forces acting together. Problems may be solved graphically or mathematically.

Figure 1.35

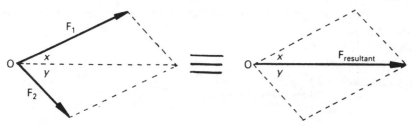

**Resolving Forces**

Remember the technique of resolution of velocities? The same process is used here.

A force is resolved into two components at right angles to each other so that the two components acting together produce the same effect as the initial single force.

Figure 1.36

*Example 1.16*

Two newton balances are used to pull an elastic band as shown in figure
1.37 *(a)*.

Figure 1.37

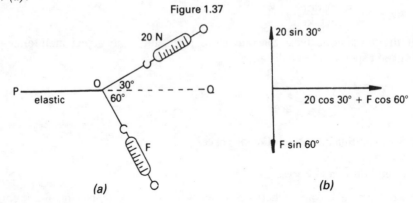

What is the size of the force $F$ and the value of the resultant force on the
elastic?

Solution:

The forces are resolved as shown in figure 1.37 *(b)*. Since the resultant must
lie along the line POQ

$F \sin 60° = 20 \sin 30°$

$\Rightarrow \quad F = 11.5 \, \text{N}$

Resultant force $= 20 \cos 30° + F \cos 60°$

$\qquad\qquad\qquad = 20 \cos 30° + 11.5 \cos 60°$

$\qquad\qquad\qquad = 23 \, \text{N}$

**Objects on Inclined Planes**

This is a situation where a force is resolved not in the vertical and horizontal
directions but perpendicular to and parallel to the inclined plane.

An object of mass $m$ on a frictionless plane inclined at an angle $\theta$ to the
horizontal has forces acting on it as shown in figure 1.38 *(a)*

Figure 1.38

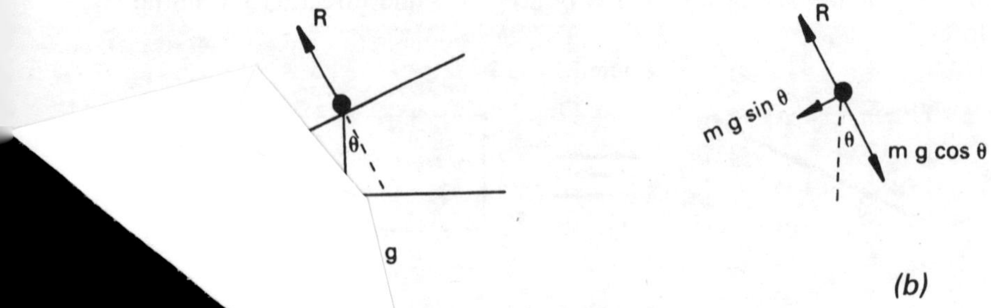

R

θ

g

R

m g sin θ

θ

m g cos θ

*(b)*

40

$mg$ is the weight of the object and $R$ is the force of the plane on the object; $R$ always acts at right angles to the plane.

In figure 1.38 *(b)* the force $mg$ has been resolved into two components; one perpendicular to the plane and one parallel to the plane. Note that diagram *(b)* is a **free body diagram** showing only the forces on the object under investigation.

Since there is no movement perpendicular to the plane $R = mg \cos \theta$.

Force down the plane $= mg \sin \theta$.

For a friction compensated plane the slope of the plane is adjusted until $mg \sin \theta$ equals the force of friction up the plane.

## 1.6 PROPERTIES OF MATTER

### 1.6.1 Density and Pressure

**Density**

The **density** of a material is defined as its mass per unit volume.

$$\text{Density } \rho = \frac{\text{mass}}{\text{volume}} = \frac{m}{V}$$

where mass is in kg and volume in $m^3$.

Density is a **scalar** with the unit $kg\ m^{-3}$.

What does the value of the density of an object tell us?

First it tells us how much matter there is in every $1\ m^3$ of the object. Compare this with the mass of the object which tells us the amount of matter in the whole object.

Probably the most important information it gives relates to the "packing" of the molecules in an object or substance. Consider a piece of expanded polystyrene with density of $16\ kg\ m^{-3}$. By squeezing the polystyrene we can easily reduce its volume to half of its original volume. Since the mass remains the same, the density of the piece of polystyrene doubles. This means that if we push the molecules of a material closer together we increase the density of the material.

How does the density of a substance in the gaseous state compare with its density in the liquid and solid states?

When a solid changes state from a solid to a liquid there is very little change in volume so since the mass remains constant the density remains constant.

The following experiment can be used to illustrate the change in volume which takes place when a substance changes from the solid state to the gaseous state.

41

A cube of solid $CO_2$ of volume 1 cm$^3$ is allowed to vaporize under water and the resulting gas collected in measuring cylinders as in figure 1.39.

Figure 1.39

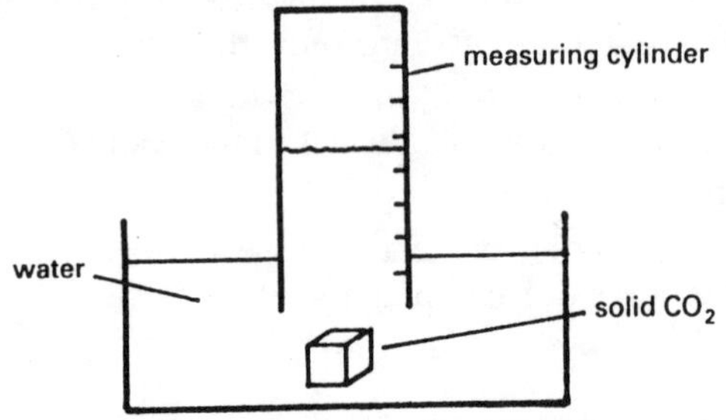

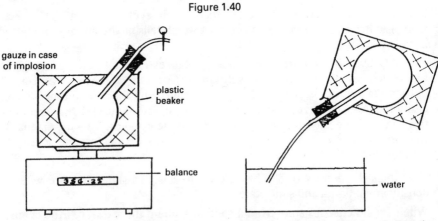

water

measuring cylinder

solid $CO_2$

It is found that approximately 1000 cm$^3$ of gas is collected.

The volume of the gaseous state is therefore 1000 times greater than that of the solid state. Since the mass remains constant this means the density of the gaseous state is 1000 times less than that of the solid state.

What happens to the particle spacing when the change takes place? Since the volume increased by a factor of 1000 the particle spacing must have increased by a factor of $\sqrt[3]{1000}$, i.e. approximately 10.

The density of air can be found experimentally using the apparatus of figure 1.40.

Figure 1.40

gauze in case of implosion

plastic beaker

balance

water

The mass $M_1$ of a 500 ml flask **and** the air inside it is found using an electronic balance which can measure to 0·01 g. A vacuum pump is now used to remove air from the flask and the new mass $M_2$ found. The mass of the air extracted is then calculated from $(M_1 - M_2)$.

The volume of the air removed by the pump can be found by immersing the flask in water and using a measuring cylinder to obtain the volume of the water which enters the flask.

The density of the air is then calculated from

$$\text{density} = \frac{\text{mass of air extracted}}{\text{volume of air extracted}}$$

## Pressure

Pressure $p$ is the force, normal to a surface, acting on unit area.

$$\text{pressure} = \frac{\text{force}}{\text{area}} \quad \text{OR} \quad p = \frac{F}{A}$$

where force is in N and area in $m^2$.

Pressure has the unit Pa (pascal) or $Nm^{-2}$.

**Note:**

1. To increase the pressure we can increase the force and/or decrease the area of contact.
2. Approximate air pressure at sea level is $1 \times 10^5$ Pa.
3. $1 \, m^2 = 10^4 \, cm^2$
   $1 \, m^3 = 10^6 \, cm^3$.

*Example 1.17*

The area of the sole of a girl's shoe is 175 $cm^2$. She has a mass of 35 kg. Calculate the pressure on the floor under one foot when it supports all of her weight.

Solution:

Force exerted on the ground $= mg = 35 \times 10 = 350 \, N$

Area of sole of shoe $= 175 \times 10^{-4} = 1.75 \times 10^{-2} \, m^2$

$$\text{pressure} = \frac{F}{A} = \frac{350}{1.75 \times 10^{-2}} = 2 \times 10^4 \text{Pa}$$

## 1.6.2 Pressure in Gases

### Kinetic Model of a Gas

In all branches of physics it is usual to form some sort of model which can be used to predict the results of further experiments.

The kinetic model of an ideal gas is based on the following assumptions:

1. the gas is composed of a large number of identical molecules
2. the molecules are small compared to the space between them
3. the molecules are in continual random motion with high speeds
4. collisions between molecules and with the walls of the container are elastic
5. there are no forces between the molecules (except during a collision).

**Note:**

*(a)* Assumptions 2 and 5 cannot be applied to liquids or solids.

*(b)* Assumption 3 is based on the random movement observed in Brownian motion experiments.

*(c)* Assumptions 2 and 3 are based on the observation of the diffusion of gas molecules.

*(d)* If assumption 4 were not true the gas would require a continuous input of energy to enable the molecules to keep moving.

*(e)* In this model the **temperature** of a gas depends on the **average kinetic energy** of a molecule of the gas. Hence if the temperature of a gas is increased the average speed of a molecule of the gas increases.

*(f)* The pressure of a gas is caused by the molecules of the gas hitting the walls of a container. When a molecule bounces off the wall of the container there is a change in momentum of the molecule (see example 1.15). This molecule therefore exerts a force on the wall and hence there is a pressure created on the walls of the container.

### Pressure/Volume Law for a Gas

What does our kinetic model predict will happen to the pressure of a gas if we change the volume of the gas while keeping its temperature constant?

Consider our sample of gas to be in a box, as in figure 1.41, which can easily be squeezed to reduce its volume.

Figure 1.41

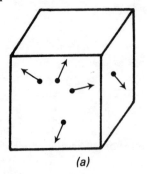

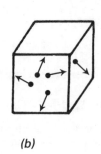

*(a)*

*(b)*

Since the temperature of the gas remains constant the average speed of a molecule of the gas remains constant. This means the molecules will undergo the same change in momentum during **each** collision in both situations. If the volume of the container decreases these collisions will happen more often. Hence the pressure on the walls of the container will increase.

The model predicts that if we decrease the volume of a gas the pressure of the gas will increase, **providing the temperature of the gas is kept constant**.

The above prediction can be easily checked using the apparatus in figure 1.42.

Figure 1.42

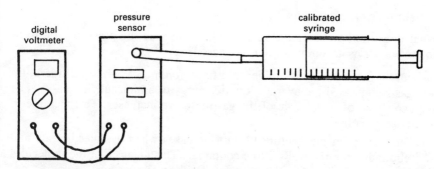

The volume of the gas trapped in the syringe can be reduced by pushing on the piston of the syringe. The volume of the gas can be read from the calibrated syringe and the pressure is recorded on the digital voltmeter connected to the pressure sensor. This can be repeated to obtain data to plot graphs of the type shown in figure 1.43.

Figure 1.43

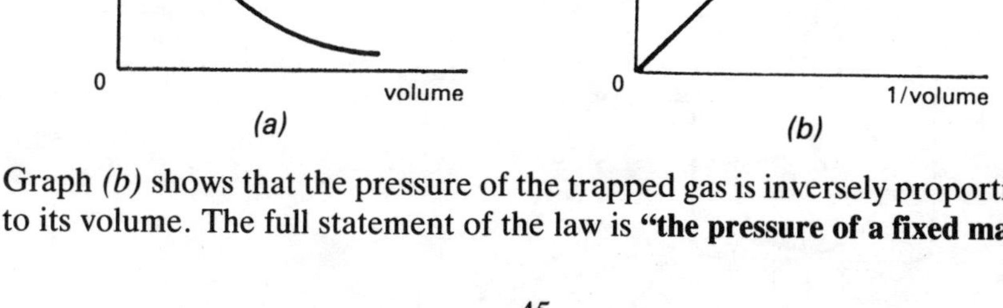

Graph *(b)* shows that the pressure of the trapped gas is inversely proportional to its volume. The full statement of the law is **"the pressure of a fixed mass of**

45

gas varies inversely as the volume provided the temperature of the gas remains constant".

Stated mathematically this gives

$pV$ = constant

OR

$p_1V_1 = p_2V_2$

where $p_1$ and $V_1$ are the initial pressure and volume of the gas and $p_2$ and $V_2$ are the final pressure and volume.

This relationship is known as Boyle's law.

## Pressure/Temperature Law for a Gas

What does the kinetic model suggest will happen to the pressure of a fixed volume of gas as its temperature is increased?

Consider a gas in a rigid container, i.e. fixed volume. When the temperature of a gas is increased the average kinetic energy of a molecule increases. The average speed of a molecule of the gas therefore increases. This increase in speed has two effects.

(a) The change in momentum ($2\ mv$) increases when a molecule hits and rebounds from the walls of the container. This means that the molecules exert a greater force on the walls, i.e. hit the walls harder.

(b) Since the molecules are moving faster, they hit the walls of the container more often.

Both of these effects lead to an increase in pressure as the temperature of the gas is increased.

This can be verified and the relationship established using the apparatus shown in figure 1.44.

Figure 1.44

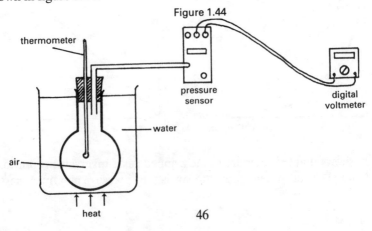

46

Readings of the pressure and temperature of the gas should be recorded as the water is heated. Care should be taken that

(a) the pressure tubing has a very small volume so that most of the gas is at the temperature of the water bath

(b) sufficient time is allowed for the temperature and pressure of the gas to stabilise before readings are taken.

The results of the experiment when plotted give a graph of the type shown in figure 1.45 (a).

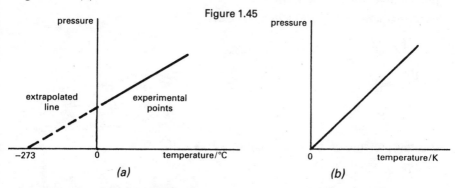

Figure 1.45

(a)

(b)

The graph of the experimental data is a straight line which does not pass through the origin. When this line is extrapolated it cuts the temperature axis at −273 °C. This implies that at a temperature of −273 °C the pressure of the fixed mass of gas would be zero. This defines the **absolute zero of temperature**. The absolute zero of temperature is used to define the **Kelvin scale of temperature**.

**temperature in kelvin = temperature in °C + 273**

Graph (b) shows the result of plotting the experimental data with the temperature converted to kelvin. If the straight line produced is extrapolated, i.e. extended, it passes through the origin. This graph establishes the law that

**"the pressure of a fixed mass of gas at constant volume varies directly as its temperature in kelvin".**

Mathematically this is

$$\frac{p}{T} = \text{constant} \quad \text{OR} \quad \frac{P_1}{T_1} = \frac{P_2}{T_2}$$

where $P_1$ and $T_1$ are the initial pressure and temperature and $P_2$ and $T_2$ are the final temperature and pressure. **The temperatures must be in kelvin.**

*Example 1.18*

The pressure in a car tyre, assumed to have a constant volume, is $2.00 \times 10^5$ Pa when the temperature is $7.00$ °C. What is the new pressure in the tyre when the temperature rises to $27.0$ °C?

Solution:

**First the temperatures must be changed to kelvin.**

Initial temperature $T_1$ in kelvin $= 7 + 273 = 280$

Final temperature $T_2$ in kelvin $= 27 + 273 = 300$

$$\frac{P_1}{T_1} = \frac{P_2}{T_2}$$

$$\frac{2 \times 10^5}{280} = \frac{P_2}{300}$$

$$P_2 = \frac{2 \times 10^5}{280} \times 300 = 2.14 \times 10^5$$

The new pressure of the air in the tyre is $2.14 \times 10^5$ Pa.

### 1.6.3 Pressure in Liquids

**Pressure at a depth in a liquid**

A point in a liquid has forces on it caused by the liquid all around it as shown in figure 1.46 (a).

Figure 1.46

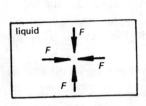

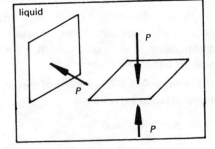

(a)                                      (b)

The forces acting on the point are the same size in all directions so any liquid at the point does not move.

48

These forces act at right angles to any surface in the liquid and cause a pressure on the surface. This is shown in figure 1.46 *(b)*.

The pressure $P$, caused by a liquid, at a point at depth $h$ in the liquid is **directly proportional** to

*(a)* the depth $h$ of the point
*(b)* the density $\rho$ of the liquid.

This gives the relationship

$P = k\rho h$

where $\rho$ is in kg m$^{-3}$, $h$ is in metres and $k$ is a constant. In fact $k$ is found to be the same as $g$ the gravitational field strength in N kg$^{-1}$. This gives the relationship

$P = \rho g h$

## Buoyancy and Flotation

For an object immersed in a liquid the pressure caused by the liquid creates a **buoyancy** or **upthrust** force on the object. This does not necessarily mean that the object will float in the liquid or on the surface of the liquid.

Now let us use our knowledge of pressure at a depth to find an expression for the buoyancy force.

Consider a cube immersed in a liquid of density $\rho$ so that its top face is at a depth $h$ below the surface of the liquid and its bottom face is at a depth $(h + t)$ as shown in figure 1.47.

Figure 1.47

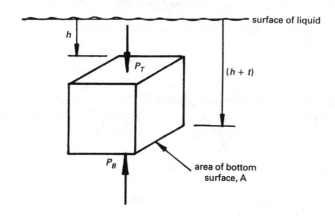

49

The downwards **pressure** $P_T$ on the top surface of the cube $= k\rho h$

The downwards **force** $F_T$ on the top surface of the cube $= P_T A = (k\rho h)A$

The upwards **pressure** $P_B$ on the bottom surface of the cube $= k\rho(h + t)$

The upwards **force** $F_B$ on the bottom surface of the cube $= P_B A = k\rho(h + t)A$

Since $h + t > h$ then the upwards force on the bottom surface is greater than the downwards force on the top surface. The resultant force, the upthrust or buoyancy force, is therefore upwards.

Upthrust force $=$ upwards force $-$ downwards force

$$= k\rho(h + t)A - k\rho hA$$
$$= k\rho tA$$

**Note:**

1.  The upthrust or buoyancy force in the above example does not depend on the depth $h$ (unless the density varies with depth).

2.  The upthrust depends on the density of the liquid. Since the density of salt water is greater than that of fresh water the upthrust on an object in salt water will be greater than the upthrust in fresh water.

3.  The presence of an upthrust force does not necessarily mean an object will float.
    Upthrust $>$ weight of object then object rises to the surface.
    Upthrust $=$ weight of object then object remains stationary.
    Upthrust $<$ weight of object then object sinks.

4.  The **total** pressure on the top surface of the cube is $\rho gh +$ atmospheric pressure.

*Example 1.19*

A cube of cork, side 2·0 cm, of weight $5·8 \times 10^{-2}$ N is held so that its top surface is 8·0 cm below the water surface in a pond. The pressure, caused by the water, on the top surface of the cube is known to be $8·0 \times 10^2$ Pa and the density of the water is $1·0 \times 10^3$ kg m$^{-3}$.

(a) What is the pressure caused by the water on the bottom surface of the block?

(b) What will happen to the cube if it is released?

Solution:

*(a)* First we find the value of $k$ in $P = k\rho h$

Pressure on top surface $= k\rho h$

$\Rightarrow \quad 8 \times 10^2 \qquad = k \times (1 \times 10^3) \times (8 \times 10^{-2})$

$\Rightarrow \qquad k \qquad = 10$

Upwards pressure on bottom surface

$\quad = k\rho h$

$\quad = 10 \times 1 \times 10^3 \times (8 \times 10^{-2} + 2 \times 10^{-2})$

$\quad = 1 \times 10^3 \text{ Pa}$

*(b)* Area of face of cube $= 2 \times 10^{-2} \times 2 \times 10^{-2}$

$\qquad\qquad\qquad\qquad\quad = 4 \times 10^{-4} \text{ m}^2$

Downwards force on top surface $=$ pressure $\times$ area

$\qquad\qquad\qquad\qquad\qquad\qquad = (8 \times 10^2) \times (4 \times 10^{-4})$

$\qquad\qquad\qquad\qquad\qquad\qquad = 3 \cdot 2 \times 10^{-1} \text{ N}$

Upwards force on bottom surface $= 1 \times 10^3 \times 4 \times 10^{-4}$

$\qquad\qquad\qquad\qquad\qquad\qquad = 4 \times 10^{-1} \text{ N}$

Buoyancy force $=$ upwards force $-$ downwards force

$\qquad\qquad\qquad = 4 \times 10^{-1} - 3 \cdot 2 \times 10^{-1}$

$\qquad\qquad\qquad = 8 \cdot 0 \times 10^{-2} \text{ N}$

The buoyancy force is greater than the weight of the cube which will therefore rise to the surface of the water.

# Chapter 2

## ELECTRICITY AND ELECTRONICS

### 2.1 CHECKLIST

#### Electric Fields

You should be able to

☐ 1. state that when a charge is in an electric field it will experience a force;

☐ 2. state that the direction of an electric field is given by the direction of the force acting on a positive charge placed in the field;

☐ 3. state that work $W$ is done when a charge $Q$ is moved in an electric field;

☐ 4. define the potential difference (p.d.) between two points in terms of the work done in moving one coulomb of charge between the points;

☐ 5. state the relationship $V = \dfrac{W}{Q}$;

☐ 6. solve problems using the relationship stated in (5) above;

☐ 7. describe the effect of a uniform electric field on the path of charged particles moving initially
   (1) parallel to the electric field
   (2) perpendicular to the electric field.

#### Resistors in Circuits

You should be able to

☐ 1. state that the free electric charges in a conductor will move if an electric field is applied across the conductor;

☐ 2. state that the rate of energy transfer, i.e. power is given by p.d. × current or equivalent expression;

☐ 3. define the electromotive force (e.m.f.) of an electrical source in terms of energy transfer;

☐ 4. state that any electrical source can be represented as a source of e.m.f. $E$ with a resistor $r$ in series (internal resistance);

☐ 5. describe an experiment to determine the e.m.f. and internal resistance of a source;

☐ 6. explain that the e.m.f. of a source is equal to the p.d. across the terminals of the source on open circuit;

☐ 7. explain how the conservation of energy leads to the sum of the e.m.f.s being equal to the sum of the p.d.s round a closed circuit;

☐ 8. solve problems involving current, p.d., power, e.m.f., internal resistance and resistance;

☐ 9. explain how a potential divider may be used to provide variable or fixed p.d.s from a given source;

☐ 10. solve problems involving potential dividers;

☐ 11. derive the expression for the total resistance of any number of resistors
(i) in series
(ii) in parallel;

☐ 12. solve circuit problems involving combinations of resistors;

☐ 13. state the relationship among the resistances in a balanced Wheatstone bridge circuit;

☐ 14. carry out calculations involving the resistances in a balanced Wheatstone bridge;

☐ 15. state that for an initially balanced Wheatstone bridge, as the value of one resistor is changed by a small amount, the out-of-balance p.d. is directly proportional to the change in resistance;

☐ 16. describe an experiment using an a.c. source of constant amplitude to obtain a graph of current against frequency in a resistive circuit;

☐ 17. state that the current in a resistive circuit does not depend on the frequency of the supply;

☐ 18. use the following correctly
e.m.f., p.d., series, parallel, internal resistance, terminal p.d., load resistor, potential divider.

**Alternating Current and Voltage**

You should be able to

☐ 1. describe how to use an oscilloscope to measure
(i) peak voltage
(ii) frequency;

☐ 2. describe an experiment to compare a.c. and d.c. sources of supply;

3. convert peak value to r.m.s. value and vice-versa for sinusoidally varying voltage and current;

4. solve problems involving r.m.s. and peak values of current and voltage;

5. use the following terms correctly
peak, peak-to-peak, root mean square (r.m.s.).

## Capacitors

You should be able to

1. state the charge $Q$ on two parallel conducting plates is directly proportional to the p.d. between the plates;

2. describe an experiment to show that the p.d. across a capacitor is directly proportional to the charge on the plates;

3. state that the capacitance $C$ is defined by the ratio of charge to p.d.;

4. state that the unit of capacitance is the farad and state that one farad is one coulomb per volt;

5. solve problems involving $C = \dfrac{Q}{V}$;

6. explain why work must be done in charging a capacitor;

7. state that the work done in charging a capacitor is given by the area under the graph of charge against p.d. for the capacitor;

8. state that the energy stored in a capacitor is given by $\frac{1}{2}$(charge $\times$ p.d.) and the equivalent expressions;

9. solve problems using the relationships connecting energy stored, capacitance, charge and p.d.;

10. draw qualitative graphs of p.d. against time for the charge and discharge of a capacitor in a d.c. circuit containing a capacitor and resistor in series;

11. draw qualitative graphs of current against time for the charge and discharge of a capacitor in a d.c. circuit containing a capacitor and resistor in series;

12. solve problems involving current and voltage in a d.c. circuit containing a capacitor and resistor in series;

13. describe an experiment using an a.c. source of constant amplitude to obtain a graph of current against frequency in a capacitive circuit;

54

☐ 14. state that the current in a capacitive circuit is directly proportional to the frequency of the source;

☐ 15. describe and explain some possible functions of a capacitor in a circuit as a store of energy or charge, or as a means of blocking d.c. signals while transmitting a.c. signals.

**Analogue electronics**

You should be able to

☐ 1. state that an op-amp can be used to increase the voltage of an electrical signal;

☐ 2. state that two of the properties of an ideal op-amp are
 (i) it has infinite input resistance, i.e. there is no input current
 (ii) there is no p.d. between the inverting and non-inverting inputs of the op-amp;

☐ 3. describe what is meant by the inverting mode of an op-amp;

☐ 4. recognize circuits where an op-amp is being used in the inverting mode;

☐ 5. derive the following expression for the gain of an op-amp used in the inverting mode $\dfrac{V_0}{V_1} = -\dfrac{R_f}{R_1}$;

☐ 6. solve problems involving the expression in (5);

☐ 7. describe what is meant by the saturation of an amplifier;

☐ 8. recognize circuits where an op-amp is being used in the differential mode;

☐ 9. state that a differential amplifier amplifies the difference in potential between its two inputs;

☐ 10. state the following expression for the gain of a differential amplifier $V_0 = (V_2 - V_1)\dfrac{R_f}{R_1}$;

☐ 11. solve problems using the expression in (10);

☐ 12. describe the operation of a circuit containing a differential amplifier and Wheatstone bridge;

☐ 13. describe how an op-amp circuit can be used with a transistor to control external devices.

55

## 2.2 PHYSICAL QUANTITIES AND UNITS

| Physical Quantity | Quantity Symbol | Unit Symbol | Unit |
|---|---|---|---|
| Electric charge | $Q$ | C | coulomb |
| Charge of electron | $e$ | C | coulomb |
| Electric potential | $V$ | V | volt |
| Electric potential difference | $V$ | V | volt |
| Electromotive force | $E$ | V | volt |
| Potential difference (alternating peak value) | $V_m, V_{pk}$ | V | volt |
| Potential difference (r.m.s. value) | $V_{r.m.s.}$ | V | volt |
| Current | $I$ | A | ampere |
| Current (alternating peak value) | $I_m, I_{pk}$ | A | ampere |
| Current (alternating r.m.s. value) | $I_{r.m.s.}$ | A | ampere |
| Resistance | $R$ | $\Omega$ | ohm |
| Capacitance | $C$ | F | farad |
| Energy | $E, W$ | J | joule |
| Power | $P$ | W | watt |
| Frequency | $f$ | Hz | hertz |

## 2.3  FORMULAE

**Electricity**

1. Electric current $I = \dfrac{Q}{t}$

2. Work done in moving a charge $= QV$

3. Electrical Power $P = VI = I^2R = \dfrac{V^2}{R}$

4. Resistance $R = \dfrac{V}{I}$

5. E.m.f. of cell $E = Ir + V_{\text{t.p.d.}}$

6. Resistors in series $R_{\text{total}} = R_1 + R_2 + R_3$

7. Resistors in parallel $\dfrac{1}{R_{\text{total}}} = \dfrac{1}{R_1} + \dfrac{1}{R_2} + \dfrac{1}{R_3}$

8. Capacitance $C = \dfrac{Q}{V}$

9. Energy stored in a capacitor $= \frac{1}{2}QV = \frac{1}{2}CV^2 = \frac{1}{2}\dfrac{Q^2}{C}$

10. $V_{\text{r.m.s.}} = \dfrac{1}{\sqrt{2}}V_{\text{m}}$ $\qquad I_{\text{r.m.s.}} = \dfrac{1}{\sqrt{2}}I_{\text{m}}$

**Analogue Electronics**

11. Amplifier gain $= \dfrac{\text{output voltage}}{\text{input voltage}} = \dfrac{V_{\text{out}}}{V_{\text{in}}}$

12. Inverting mode amplifier gain $= \dfrac{V_0}{V_1} = -\dfrac{R_f}{R_1}$

13. Differential mode amplifier output $V_0 = (V_2 - V_1)\dfrac{R_f}{R_1}$

## 2.4  ELECTRIC FIELD

### 2.4.1  Field Strength and Potential Difference

The concept of a field is used to describe the behaviour of an electric charge when it is under the influence of forces caused by other electric charges. The presence of an electric field at a point in space may be detected by the movement of an electric charge when placed at that point.

The direction of an electric field at a point is given by the direction of the force acting on a positive charge placed at that point. Field lines are drawn to show the path this charge would take in the field.

Figure 2.1

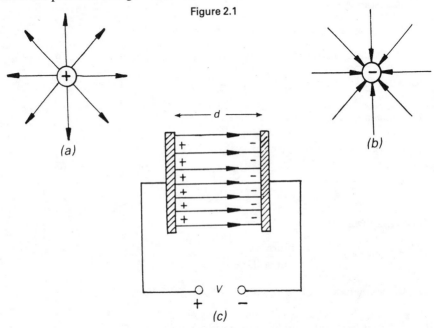

*(a)*

*(b)*

*(c)*

Figure 2.1 shows the electric field lines

*(a)*  around a point positive charge (a point charge does not occupy any space)

*(b)*  around a point negative charge

*(c)*  between two charged parallel conducting plates.

Situations *(a)* and *(b)* are examples of **radial fields**: the distance between the field lines increases with distance from the charge indicating that the field is becoming weaker with increasing distance from the charge.

In *(c)* the electric field lines are equidistant indicating that the field is **uniform** or constant between the plates.

The **potential difference p.d.** $V$ between two points in an electric field is defined as the work $W$ done in moving a unit positive charge between the two points against the direction of the field lines. (If the positive charge is moved in the direction of the electric field lines the electric field would be doing work.) Hence the relationship

$$V = \frac{W}{Q} \text{ or } W = QV$$

*Example 2.1*

Two parallel conducting plates, A and B, are $2 \cdot 0 \times 10^{-2}$ m apart in a vacuum. There is a p.d. of $4 \cdot 0$ kV applied across them as shown in figure 2.2.

Figure 2.2

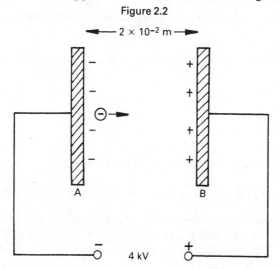

Calculate

(a) the kinetic energy gained by an electron moving from the negatively charged plate to the positively charged plate

(b) the speed of the electron just before it strikes plate B

(c) the size of the force exerted by the electric field on the electron.

Charge on electron = $1 \cdot 6 \times 10^{-19}$ C
Mass of electron   = $9 \cdot 1 \times 10^{-31}$ kg

Solution:

(a) the electron gains kinetic energy as it is accelerated along a field line.

gain in $E_k$ = work done in moving between plates A and B
$$= QV$$
$$= 1 \cdot 6 \times 10^{-19} \times 4 \times 10^3$$
$$= 6 \cdot 4 \times 10^{-16} \text{ J}$$

59

*(b)* Gain in kinetic energy $= 1/2\ m\ v^2$

$$6.4 \times 10^{-16} = 1/2 \times 9.1 \times 10^{-31} \times v^2$$

$\Rightarrow \qquad\qquad\qquad v^2 = 1.406 \times 10^{-15}$

$\Rightarrow \qquad\qquad\qquad v\ = 3.7 \times 10^7\ m\ s^{-1}$

*(c)* Electric force between plates A and B is constant

$\Rightarrow$ Work done by electric field in moving electron between plates =
electric force $\times$ distance

also

Work done by electric field in moving electron between plates =
gain in kinetic energy of electron

$\Rightarrow$ gain in kinetic energy of electron = electric force $\times$ distance

$\Rightarrow \qquad\qquad 6.4 \times 10^{-16} = F \times 2 \times 10^{-2}$

$\Rightarrow \qquad\qquad\qquad F = 3.2 \times 10^{-14}\ N$

### 2.4.2 Moving Charges in a Uniform Electric Field

### (A) INITIAL VELOCITY OF CHARGE PARALLEL TO FIELD LINES

If a charge has an initial velocity along a field line, in a uniform field, it continues to move, with a constant acceleration, along that field line. In example 2.1 the kinetic energy gained is $6.4 \times 10^{-16}$ J. The total kinetic energy on reaching plate B is:

total $E_k$ = initial $E_k$ + gain in $E_k$

Have you realised that this is the same concept as movement of a mass along a gravitational field line.

Usually, at this level, the effect of the gravitational force acting on the mass of the charge is neglected.

## (B) INITIAL VELOCITY OF CHARGE PERPENDICULAR TO FIELD LINES.

Figure 2.3 shows an electron with an initial velocity perpendicular to the electric field lines between two parallel charged conducting plates.

Figure 2.3

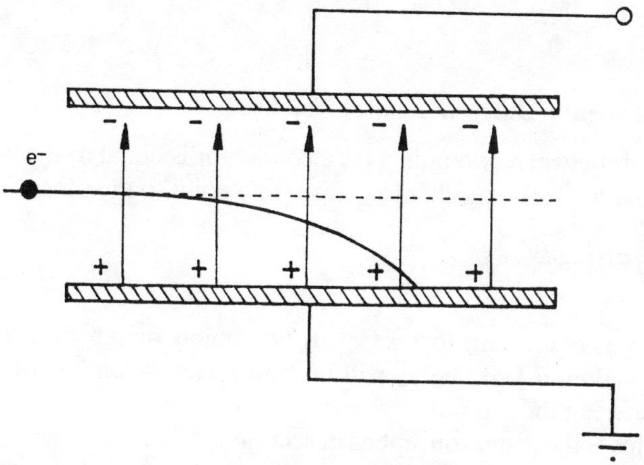

The plates must be conductors otherwise the charge would not be evenly distributed and the field would not be uniform.

If there is a vacuum between the plates and no field lines in the $x$-direction there will be no acceleration or deceleration in the $x$-direction. Because the field lines are in the positive $y$-direction there will be an electric field force acting on the electron in the negative $y$-direction. (**Remember field lines show the direction of movement of positive charges.**) This causes a **constant** acceleration $a_y$ in the negative $y$-direction. This situation is similar to that of projectiles in a uniform gravitational field.

## 2.5 RESISTORS IN CIRCUITS

### 2.5.1 Charge and Current

In metals the electrons close to the nucleus are tightly bound to the nucleus forming positive **metal ions**. The electrons furthest from the nucleus are free to move through the metal and are called **conduction electrons**. If a conductor has an electric field applied across it the conduction electrons "drift" towards the more positive end of the conductor. The electric field is created by

61

applying a potential difference $V$ across the ends of the conductor by means of a battery or power supply.

**Electric current $I$, measured in amperes, is the rate of flow of charge $Q$ in the conductor.**

$$I = \frac{Q}{t}$$

$$\Rightarrow Q = It$$

### 2.5.2 Potential Difference and Resistance

The p.d. between two points on a conductor is equal to the work done $W$ per unit charge in moving charge $Q$ from one point to the other. Hence.

$$V = \frac{W}{Q} \text{ giving } W = QV$$

**Note:**

(a) 1 V is equivalent to 1 J C$^{-1}$. If two points on a conductor have a p.d. of 6 V then 6 J of energy will be transferred when 1 C of charge is moved between these points.

(b) This is the same concept as in section 2.4.1.

The energy $W$ which moves the charge through the conductor must be supplied by a power supply or battery.

Figure 2.4

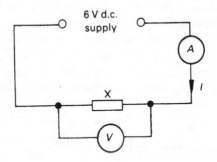

If charge Q passes through the resistor X in figure 2.4 in $t$ seconds then

$$W = VQ$$

Power $P$ dissipated in resistor $= \frac{W}{t} = V\frac{Q}{t} = VI$

$$\Rightarrow P = VI$$

The resistance $R$ to the flow of charge in a conductor is the ratio of the p.d. across the conductor to the current in it.

$$R = \frac{V}{I} \quad \text{giving} \quad V = IR$$

It is this resistance to the flow of charge which causes the conductor to heat up when charge flows in it. The circuit of figure 2.4 can be used to obtain values of $V$ and $I$ thus allowing $R$ to be calculated. In this circuit it is assumed that the ammeter has zero resistance and the voltmeter has infinite resistance.

Ohm's Law states "the current in a conductor is directly proportional to the p.d. across it **providing the temperature remains constant**".

If the p.d. $V$ across the component is plotted on the $y$-axis and the current $I$ on the $x$-axis then the gradient of the graph at a point will give the resistance at the corresponding point on the graph.

Figure 2.5

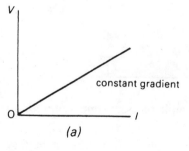

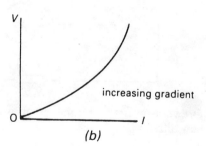

(a)            (b)

In figure 2.5 (a) the gradient and hence the resistance is constant for all values of the current in the component. In (b) the gradient and hence the resistance increases as the current in the component increases. The component could be the filament of a lamp whose temperature increases as the current in it increases.

Note the relationship $V = IR$ leads to alternative statements of electrical power

$$P = VI$$
$$\Rightarrow P = I^2R \text{ since } V = IR$$
$$\Rightarrow P = \frac{V^2}{R} \text{ since } I = \frac{V}{R}$$

## 2.5.2 E.M.F. and Internal Resistance

The electromotive force (e.m.f.) $E$ of a source, power supply or battery, is the energy per coulomb converted when charge passes through the source. The unit of e.m.f. is the volt or joule per coulomb.

In figure 2.4 the supply delivers 6 J of energy for every one coulomb that passes around the circuit. If the battery is ideal, with no energy being converted to heat inside it, then the 6 J per coulomb would be converted to heat in component X, if this is a resistor. In a real source some energy is transferred to heat in the source when charge flows in it. A real source is represented by an ideal source of e.m.f. in series with a resistor $r$, (internal resistance of the source), as in figure 2.6.

### Figure 2.6

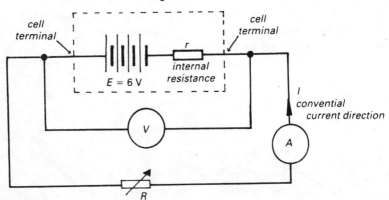

Drawn as in figure 2.6 the circuit is a very simple one and should present no new difficulties.

By conservation of energy, the energy per coulomb converted by the battery must equal the sum of the energies per coulomb converted in $r$ and $R$.

$$E = \text{p.d. across } r + \text{p.d. across } R$$
$$= Ir + IR$$

The voltmeter in figure 2.6 measures the p.d. across the terminals of the battery, i.e. the terminal potential difference ($V_{\text{t.p.d.}}$)

$$E = Ir + V_{\text{t.p.d.}}$$
$$\Rightarrow V_{\text{t.p.d.}} = E - Ir$$

Note that $V_{\text{t.p.d.}}$ is equal to the e.m.f. $E$ when there is no current in the circuit; this is shown in the above equation by placing $I = 0$. The e.m.f. of a supply could therefore be measured by connecting a **very** high resistance voltmeter across the supply.

The circuit of figure 2.6 can be used to find the e.m.f. and the internal resistance of the battery. Different currents can be produced in the circuit, by varying $R$, and the corresponding values of $V_{\text{t.p.d.}}$ measured. A graph is plotted as in figure 2.7.

Figure 2.7

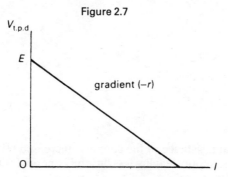

The equation $V_{\text{t.p.d.}} = E - Ir$ can be rewritten as $V_{\text{t.p.d.}} = (-r)\,I + E$ and compared with the equation of a straight line $y = mx + c$.

Hence the gradient of the graph is $(-r)$ and the intercept on the $y$-axis gives the e.m.f. of the supply.

Note that the power dissipated in the battery is $I^2r$ and increases as more current is drawn from the cell. This is wasted energy as it only increases the temperature of the cell.

*Example 2.2*

A battery of e.m.f. 12 $V$ has a p.d. of 10 $V$ across its terminals when a lamp is connected to it as shown in figure 2.8. There is a current of 0·40 A in the lamp.

Figure 2.8

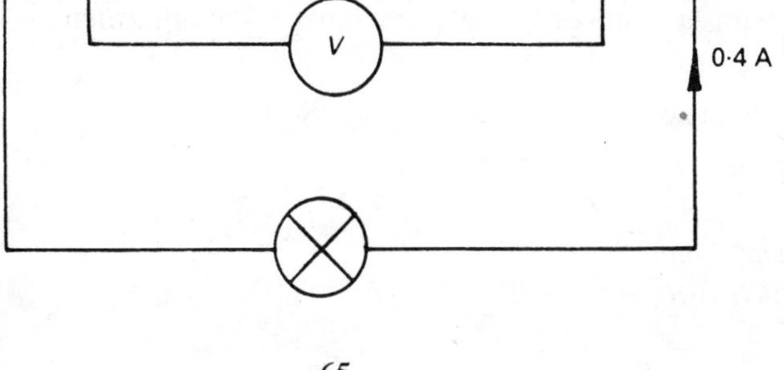

65

c

Find *(a)* the internal resistance of the battery and *(b)* the energy "lost" inside the battery in 20 *s*.

Solution:

*(a)*  $E = V_{\text{t.p.d.}} + Ir$

$\Rightarrow 12 = 10 + 0\cdot4 \times r$

$\Rightarrow r = 5\Omega$

*(b)* Energy "lost" $= Pt$

$= I^2r \times 20$

$= (0\cdot4)^2 \times 5 \times 20$

$= 16 \text{ J}$

**Note:**

(1) If the internal resistance of the supply is increased relatively more energy is "lost" in the supply leaving less "useful" energy for the load *R*.

(2) The internal resistance limits the maximum current supplied by the cell. If the cell in figure 2.8 is short-circuited the current $I = \dfrac{E}{r} = \dfrac{12}{5} = 2\cdot4 \text{ A}$.

### 2.5.4 Combinations of Resistors

#### (A) RESISTORS IN SERIES

Figure 2.9

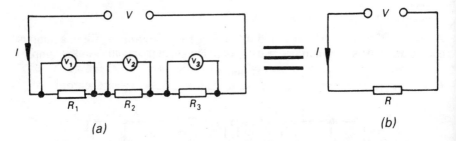

*(a)*  *(b)*

The problem is to find a single resistor *R* which will have the **same** effect in the circuit as the three resistors $R_1$, $R_2$ and $R_3$ connected in series.

By conservation of energy [remember 1 *V* is equivalent to 1 J C$^{-1}$].

$V = V_1 + V_2 + V_3$

Since the current is the same in $R_1$, $R_2$ and $R_3$

$\Rightarrow \dfrac{V}{I} = \dfrac{V_1}{I} + \dfrac{V_2}{I} + \dfrac{V_3}{I}$

Using Ohm's Law

$\Rightarrow R = R_1 + R_2 + R_3$

66

# (B) RESISTORS IN PARALLEL

Figure 2.10

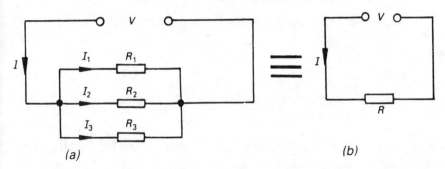

(a)                                                   (b)

The resistor $R$ in figure 2.10 *(b)* must give the same effect as resistors $R_1$, $R_2$ and $R_3$ connected in parallel as in *(a)*.

In circuit *(a)*, the charge which leaves one terminal of the supply must arrive at the other terminal. This is conservation of charge.

$$I = I_1 + I_2 + I_3$$
$$\Rightarrow \frac{V}{R} = \frac{V}{R_1} + \frac{V}{R_2} + \frac{V}{R_3}$$
$$\Rightarrow \frac{1}{R} = \frac{1}{R_1} + \frac{1}{R_2} + \frac{1}{R_3}$$

**Note:**

(1) For resistors in parallel the effective resistance is always less than the smallest of the individual resistances. This is because any resistor placed in parallel to an existing one will give another possible current path.

(2) When resistors are connected in parallel the p.d. across each of them is the same.

*Example 2.3*

Calculate the total resistance of the arrangement of resistors shown in figure 2.11 *(a)*.

Figure 2.11

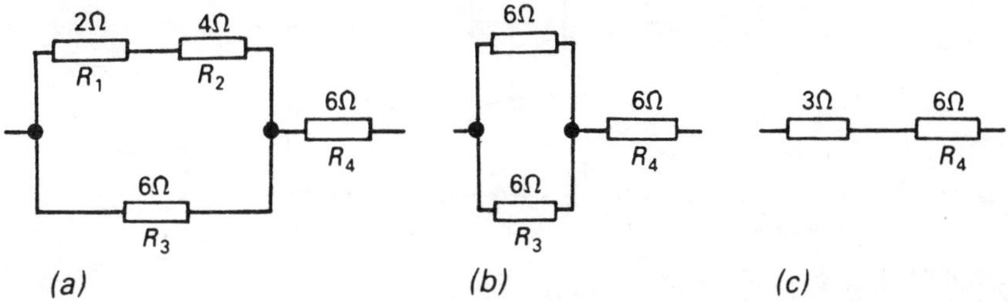

(a)                    (b)                    (c)

First the resistors in series.

The total resistance of the $2\Omega$ and $4\Omega$ resistors in series is $6\Omega$.

There is therefore effectively a $6\Omega$ resistor in parallel with $R_3$. From *(b)*

$$\frac{1}{R} = \frac{1}{6} + \frac{1}{6} = \frac{2}{6}$$
$$\Rightarrow R = 3\Omega$$

The resistor $R_4$ is effectively in series with a $3\Omega$ resistor as in *(c)*. The total resistance is therefore $9\Omega$.

**Note:** two resistors each of resistance $X$ when connected in parallel are equivalent to a single resistor of value $X/2$.

### 2.5.5 Potential and Potential Divider

In electronics the concept of earthing is important. If a point in a circuit is earthed, i.e. connected to the earth terminal of a power supply then the potential of this point is 0 V. The **potential** at any other point in the circuit is measured with reference to this point.

Figure 2.12

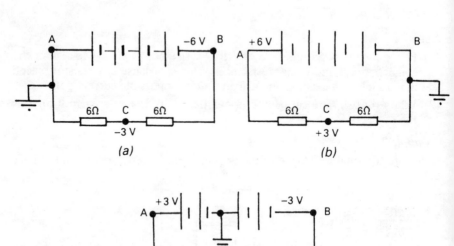

*(a)*

*(b)*

*(c)*

68

In figure 2.12 *(a)*, *(b)* and *(c)* the cells each have e.m.f. 1·5 V and to isolate the concept of potential in the problem the internal resistance of each cell is considered to be very small. The total circuit resistance is 12Ω giving a current of 0·5 A in the resistors. The p.d. across each resistor is then 3 V. In circuits *(a)*, *(b)* and *(c)* the potentials at point A are different (similarly for B and C) yet the potential differences between corresponding points are the same.

A **potential divider** is used to supply different p.d.s from one source of constant e.m.f.

Figure 2.13

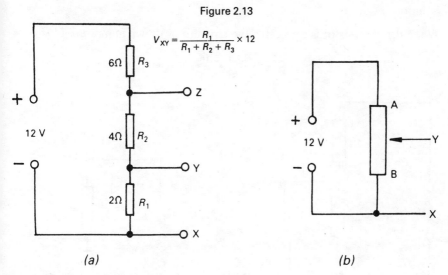

$$V_{XY} = \frac{R_1}{R_1 + R_2 + R_3} \times 12$$

*(a)*

*(b)*

In figure 2.13 *(a)* the total circuit resistance is equal to 12Ω hence there is a current of 1 A in the circuit.

p.d. across $XY = IR_1$ $\qquad = 2\,V$

p.d. across $XZ = I(R_1 + R_2) = 6\,V$

Hence the p.d.s of 2 V and 6 V can be obtained from the original 12 V supply.

Note that taking current from the circuit at XY or XZ will alter the p.d.

To obtain **variable** p.d.s a variable resistor is used as in *(b)*. When the sliding contact is at point A the p.d. across XY is 12 V and when it is at B the p.d. across XY is 0 V. Therefore **any** p.d. between 0 V and 12 V can be obtained across the contacts XY.

Note that if the p.d. in the potential divider is to remain fixed then any component connected across it must have a high resistance compared to the resistors in the potential divider. If this seems difficult to understand the following example should help!

*Example 2.4*

A resistance of 6Ω is connected across XZ in figure 2.13 *(a)*. What is the new value of the p.d. between the points X and Z.

Solution:

When the 6Ω resistor is connected the circuit is as shown in figure 2.14 *(b)*.

Figure 2.14

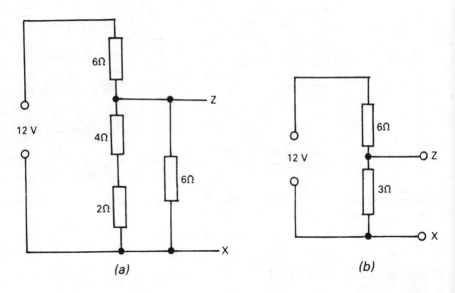

(a)                    (b)

The total resistance of the circuit is now found to be 9Ω as in example 2.3. The total current from the supply is $I = V/R = 12/9 = 1.33$ A. The p.d. between X and Z $= IR = 1.33 \times 3 = 4$ V

The p.d. across XZ has changed from 6 V to 4 V by adding in this load resistor of 6Ω.

## 2.5.6 Wheatstone Bridge

A Wheatstone bridge circuit is an arrangement of resistors which is used to find the values of unknown resistors or as an input circuit in electronics.

Figure 2.15

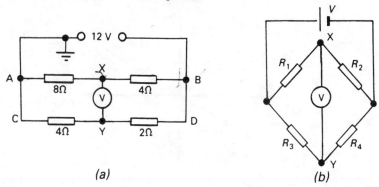

(a)                                        (b)

First consider the circuit of figure 2.15 (a). You will see that the bridge is simply two potential divider circuits connected across the 12 V supply. You can work out the potential at X and Y using the method in 2.5.5 or you might prefer the following way.

The resistance of the current path AXB is 12 Ω therefore the current in this path is 1 A. The p.d. across the 8 Ω resistor is 8 V therefore the potential of the point X is +8 V.

Similarly the potential at point Y is +8 V and there is therefore no p.d. between points X and Y. When this situation is achieved the voltmeter reading is zero and the bridge is said to be **balanced**.

**Note:**
1.  If the value of the 8 Ω resistor is increased the potential of point X becomes greater than +8 V, i.e. point X is more positive than point Y.
2.  If this same resistance is decreased, the p.d. between X and Y becomes negative.

Why is this important? Well consider a bridge which is initially balanced and then the value of one of the resistances changes. We can tell by observing the **sign** of the p.d. between X and Y whether the resistance has increased or decreased.

The relationship among the resistors in the Wheatstone bridge, drawn as in figure 2.15 (b), **if it is balanced** is

$$\frac{R_1}{R_2} = \frac{R_3}{R_4} \quad \text{OR} \quad \frac{R_1}{R_3} = \frac{R_2}{R_4}$$

Figure 2.16 shows the variation of the p.d. between X and Y as one of the resistors is changed by **small** amounts from its value when the bridge is balanced.

Figure 2.16

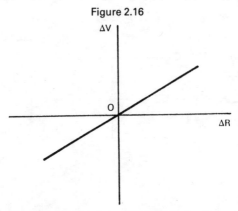

ΔR is the amount that the resistance is **different** from the value for balance of the bridge. This **linear** variation of p.d. with change in resistance is used in control systems in electronics. One of the resistors, say $R_4$, can be replaced by a sensor (light-dependent resistor (L.D.R.) for applications in light or by a thermistor for heating control applications). The circuit is balanced for normal conditions by the correct selection of resistors. The circuit will then sense the amount by which the bridge becomes off-balance and whether the resistance of the sensor has increased or decreased.

## 2.6 ALTERNATING CURRENT AND VOLTAGE

### 2.6.1 Measurement of Frequency using an Oscilloscope

Frequency $f$ is the number of complete cycles per second of the alternating current.

Period $T$ is the time for one complete cycle ... $T = 1/f$.

Although there are digital frequency meters, an oscilloscope is often used to measure the frequency of an a.c. source. The y-input of the oscilloscope is connected across the source whose frequency is to be measured. The time-base setting of the oscilloscope is then varied until a trace is obtained such that the cycles of the waveform are distinct as in figure 2.17.

72

Figure 2.17

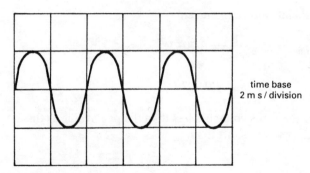

time base
2 m s / division

The frequency can then be calculated as follows:

total length of trace = 6 divisions

$\Rightarrow$ total time for trace = $6 \times 2 = 12$ m s

In this time there are 3 complete cycles

$\Rightarrow$ time for 1 cycle (i.e. period) is 4 m s

$\Rightarrow$ frequency $= \dfrac{1}{\text{period}} = \dfrac{1}{4 \times 10^{-3}} = 250$ Hz

## 2.6.2 R.M.S. Voltage

Peak or amplitude $V_{pk}$ or $I_{pk}$ is the maximum value of the alternating voltage or current.

Figure 2.18

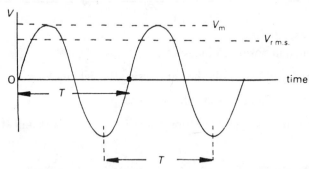

As the sinusoidal voltage varies between a maximum and minimum value it is useful to define an effective or r.m.s (root mean square) voltage.

**Root mean square voltage $V_{r.m.s}$ of an a.c. supply is the value of the d.c. voltage which will give the same dissipation of power in a fixed resistor as the a.c. voltage.**

73

These quantities are shown in figure 2.18 for a sinusoidal alternating voltage.

For a sinusoidal voltage or current

$$V_{\text{r.m.s}} = V_{\text{pk}} \frac{1}{\sqrt{2}} = 0{\cdot}707\,V_{\text{pk}}$$

$$I_{\text{r.m.s}} = I_{\text{pk}} \frac{1}{\sqrt{2}} = 0{\cdot}707\,I_{\text{pk}}$$

Remember the r.m.s voltage is less than the peak value as the a.c. voltage has a value $V_m$ for a very short time.

### 2.6.3 Experimental Comparison of $V_{\text{r.m.s}}$ and $V_{\text{pk}}$

The circuit and apparatus in figure 2.19 can be used to verify the relationship between $V_{\text{r.m.s}}$ and $V_{\text{pk}}$

Figure 2.19

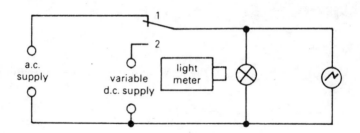

With the switch in position 1 measure:

*(a)* the intensity of light from the lamp, using the light meter

*(b)* $V_{\text{pk}}$ of the a.c. source, using the oscilloscope.

Place the switch in position 2 to substitute the variable d.c. supply for the a.c. supply then:

*(a)* vary the d.c. voltage until the light intensity from the lamp is the same as previously measured

*(b)* record the value $V_{\text{dc}}$ of the d.c. voltage. It should be found that $V_{\text{dc}} = 0{\cdot}7\,V_{\text{pk}}$.

74

## 2.7 CAPACITORS

### 2.7.1 Capacitors, Charge and Potential Difference

First, without considering its construction think of a capacitor as a component which stores electric charge. The capacitance of a capacitor is the electric charge stored per unit p.d. across the capacitor.

$$C = \frac{Q}{V}$$

$Q$ is charge stored in coulombs
$V$ is p.d. across the capacitor
$C$ is the capacitance in farads

$$\Rightarrow Q = VC$$

**Note:**

1. The higher the capacitance then the greater is the charge stored for a given p.d.
2. The higher the capacitance then the lower is the p.d. for a given charge stored.

This relationship can be investigated by using the circuit of figure 2.20.

Figure 2.20

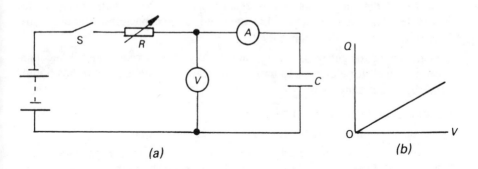

(a)         (b)

The symbol for the capacitor $C$ illustrates that in its simplest form a capacitor can be two conducting plates separated by insulating material.

When switch S is closed the ammeter indicates that there is a flow of charge to the capacitor $C$ and that this current decreases with time. By gradually **decreasing** the value of the variable resistor the **current $I$ to the capacitor can be kept constant**. Readings of the p.d. $V$ are taken at intervals of time. The charge on the capacitor at these times can be calculated using $Q = It$ and a graph such as in figure 2.20 *(b)* obtained. The capacitance is given by the gradient $Q/V$ of the graph (since $Q = VC$).

### 2.7.2 Charge and Discharge of a Capacitor

Figure 2.21 shows a circuit for investigating the charge and discharge of a capacitor.

Figure 2.21

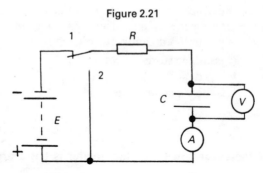

The charge on the capacitor $C$ and the p.d. across it are initially zero. When switch S is moved to position 1 electrons will flow from the supply to the top plate of the capacitor. The electrons on the top plate repel electrons from the bottom plate which then move to the positive of the supply. The only opposition to this flow of charge is that caused by $R$: hence the initial current $I = E/R$ if the supply has zero internal resistance. Note that no charge can move from the top plate to the bottom plate of the capacitor as the plates are separated by insulating material.

As the capacitor charges, the p.d. across its plates increases and it becomes more difficult for electrons to move to the capacitor against the opposition of the charges already there.

During **charging** of a capacitor:

1. the charging current decreases to zero from an initial value $E/R$,
2. the p.d. across the capacitor increases from 0 to a maximum value $E$, the e.m.f. of the supply. The capacitor is now fully charged,
3. the p.d. across $R$ decreases to zero as the charging current decreases.
4. the sum of the p.d. across the capacitor and the p.d. across $R$ equals the e.m.f. $E$ of the supply at all times.

If now the switch is moved to position 2 the capacitor discharges as electrons pass from the top plate of the capacitor, through $R$ and the ammeter, to the bottom plate of the capacitor. This will give an initial current $I = E/R$ if the capacitor has been fully charged. It is sometimes helpful to think of the capacitor in this application as similar to a rechargeable cell.

76

During **discharge** of the capacitor

1. the discharge current decreases to zero from an initial value of $E/R$,
2. the p.d. across the capacitor decreases from $E$ to 0,
3. the p.d. across $R$ decreases from $E$ to zero as the current in the circuit decreases,
4. in figure 2.21 electrons move towards the bottom plate hence the ammeter shows a change in direction of current flow from that during the charging process.
5. the p.d. across the capacitor always equals the p.d. across $R$.

The graphs of figure 2.22 show the variation of p.d. and current during charging and discharging of a capacitor.

Figure 2.22

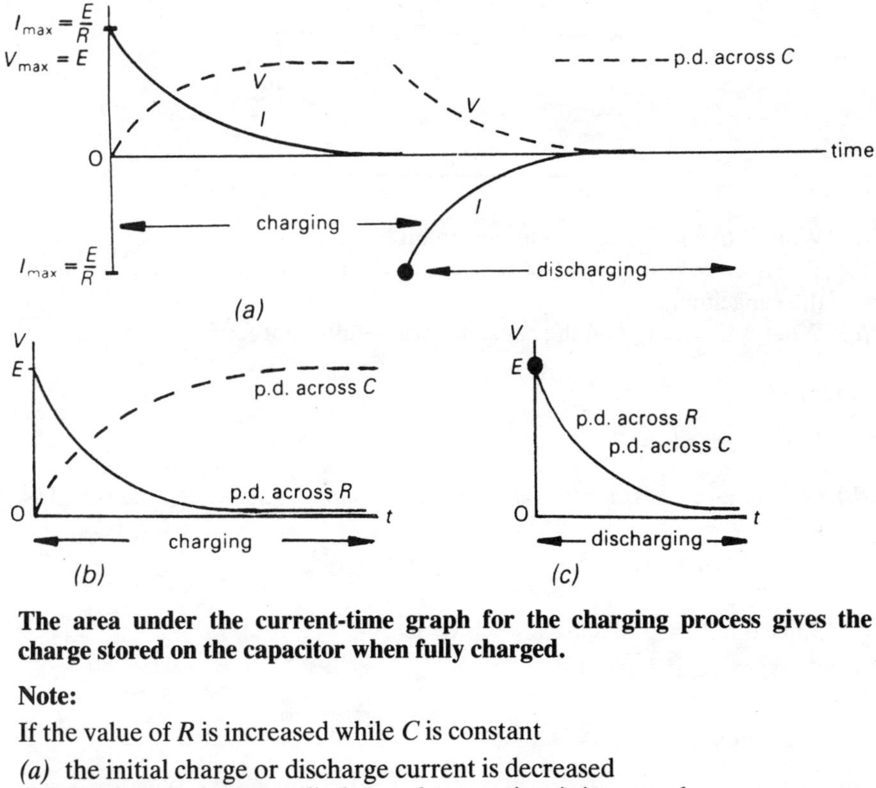

The area under the current-time graph for the charging process gives the charge stored on the capacitor when fully charged.

**Note:**

If the value of $R$ is increased while $C$ is constant

(a) the initial charge or discharge current is decreased
(b) the time to charge or discharge the capacitor is increased
(c) the area under the $I$-$t$ graph is the same as before as the same amount of charge is required to fully charge the capacitor.

If the value of $C$ is increased, while $R$ is constant

(a) the initial current during charge and discharge is unaltered
(b) the capacitor takes a longer time to charge to the same p.d. as it requires a greater charge to do so
(c) the area under the $I$-$t$ graph will be greater as the charge required for a given p.d. will be greater.

The following example should help clarify the above points.

*Example 2.5*

In the circuit shown in figure 2.23 the capacitor is initially uncharged. Switch S is now closed.

Figure 2.23

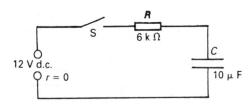

(a) What is the initial current in the circuit?
(b) When there is a current of 0·5 mA in the circuit what is the p.d. across the capacitor?
(c) What is the charge on the capacitor when fully charged?

Solution:

(a) Initial current $I = E/R = \dfrac{12}{6 \times 10^3} = 2\,\text{mA}$

(b) When there is a current of 0·5 m A in the circuit the p.d. across $R$ will be given by

$$\text{p.d. across } R = IR = 0\text{·}5 \times 10^{-3} \times 6 \times 10^3$$
$$= 3\,\text{V}$$

Since e.m.f. = p.d. across $R$ + p.d. across $C$
$$\Rightarrow \quad E = V_R + V_C$$
$$\Rightarrow \quad 12 = 3 \ + V_C$$
p.d. across capacitor = 9 V

(c) $Q = VC$
$$= 12 \times 10 \times 10^{-6} = 1\text{·}2 \times 10^{-4}$$
Charge on capacitor is $1\text{·}2 \times 10^{-4}\,\text{C}$.

78

### 2.7.3 Energy Stored in a Capacitor

When charge has been transferred from the power supply to the capacitor then energy will be stored in the capacitor as electric field energy.

Figure 2.24

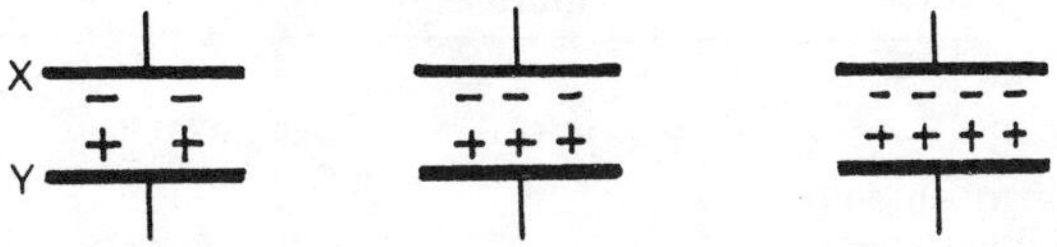

As the capacitor in figure 2.24 is charging up, plate X becomes increasingly negative while plate Y becomes increasingly positive as electrons are repelled from it to the supply. As plate X becomes more negative work must be done to put more electrons on it against the increasing force from the electrons already there. **The work done during the charging process must be equal to the energy stored in the capacitor (as given by the area under the graph in figure 2.25).**

Figure 2.25

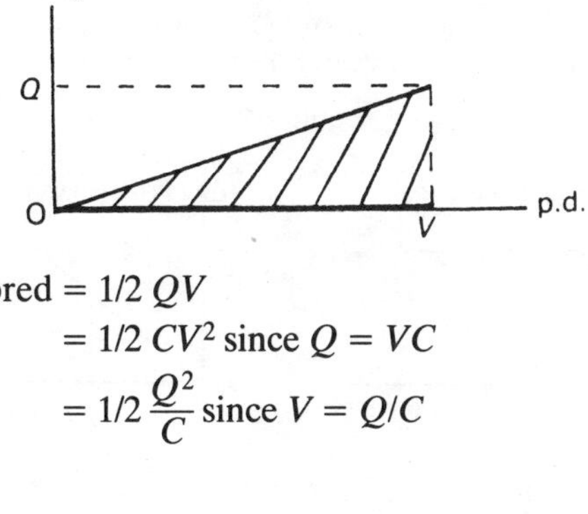

$$\text{Energy stored} = 1/2\ QV$$
$$= 1/2\ CV^2 \text{ since } Q = VC$$
$$= 1/2\ \frac{Q^2}{C} \text{ since } V = Q/C$$

**Note:**

1. Contrast the formula $W = 1/2\ QV$ with that obtained ($W = QV$) for a charge $Q$ moving between two points with **constant** p.d. In the first situation $V$ is increasing as more charge is added to the capacitor while in the second the p.d. between the points remains fixed as the charge is moved between the points.

2. If a capacitor is fully charged then when a resistor is placed across the terminals of the capacitor the electrical energy stored in the capacitor will be dissipated as heat in the resistor. The **rate of release of energy from the capacitor will depend on the value of the resistor but the total energy released will remain constant.**

### 2.7.4 Capacitors and Resistors in A.C. Circuits

How does the frequency of an electrical source affect the current in a circuit containing a resistor or capacitor? The circuit of figure 2.26 can be used to investigate this.

Figure 2.26

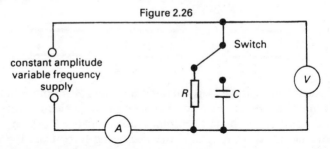

The electrical source used is a calibrated signal generator. The ammeter and voltmeter are a.c. meters which indicate r.m.s. values. The component to be used is first selected using the switch. The voltmeter can be used to check that the r.m.s. (and hence amplitude) of the output voltage of the supply is constant at different frequencies. The current in the component is then measured for various frequencies of the source and a current-frequency graph plotted from the results as shown in figure 2.27.

Figure 2.27

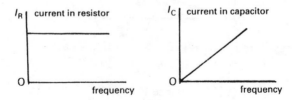

The graphs show that:
1. the current in the resistor does not depend on the frequency of the source;
2. the current in the circuit with the capacitor is directly proportional to the frequency of the source.

How are these results related to theory?

First consider that when the source is a d.c. source the frequency $f$ of the source is zero.

For a capacitor when a d.c. supply ($f = 0$) is used there is no current in the circuit after the initial charging process. When an a.c. supply is used the capacitor will be alternately charging and discharging hence there is a current in the circuit although no flow of charge through the actual capacitor.

80

### 2.7.5 Uses of Capacitors

1. A capacitor can be used to "block" a d.c. signal but allow the passage of an a.c. signal. This allows amplification of only the a.c. part of a signal as in figure 2.28.

Figure 2.28

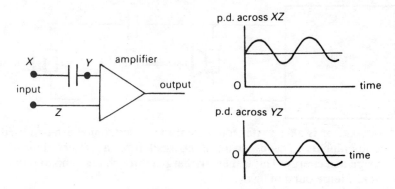

2. After rectification of a.c. a capacitor is used as in figure 2.29 to produce a "smooth" d.c. voltage. With switch S open the p.d. across $R$ is shown in (b) and with S closed the p.d. is as shown in (c).

Figure 2.29

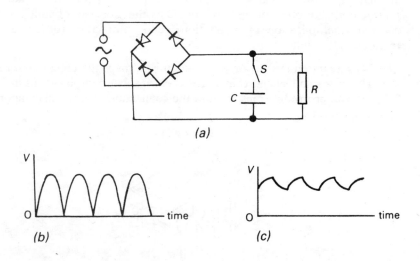

3. In a simple hi-fi system there are two loudspeakers; one which is efficient at high frequencies and one which is suitable for lower frequencies. The capacitor in the circuit of figure 2.30 is used to allow the currents of higher frequency to pass to loudspeaker 2 while the lower frequencies pass through loudspeaker 1.

Figure 2.30

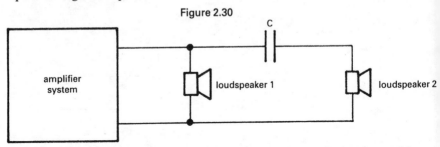

4. A capacitor is also a vital component in an electronic flash-gun used by photographers. The capacitor is charged from a battery thus storing charge and energy. This is then discharged through the lamp to produce a short intense burst of light.

## 2.8 ANALOGUE ELECTRONICS

### 2.8.1 Basic Characteristics

**Operational amplifiers** or **op**-amps were designed to process electrical signals in analogue form to carry out the mathematical **op**erations of addition, subtraction, multiplication and division. Only the processes of multiplication, division (multiplication by a fraction), and subtraction (difference) are required in this unit.

The 741 integrated circuit (or **IC**) op-amp is perhaps the commonest one in use. This is a small silicon chip which is encapsulated in plastic, as in figure 2.31 *(a)* with protruding pins to allow the connection of external components such as resistors.

Figure 2.31

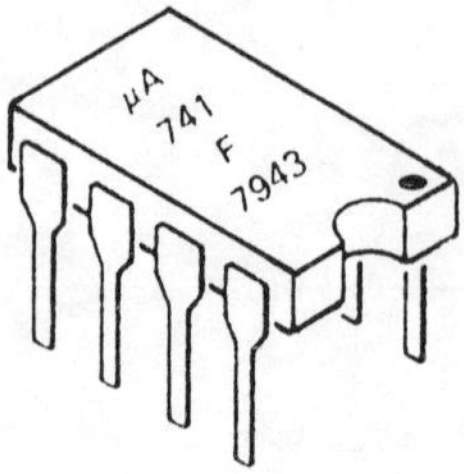

μA
741
F
7943

*(a)*

82

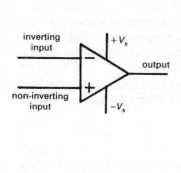

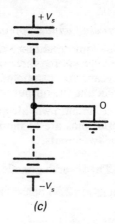

(b)                      (c)

The symbol for an op-amp is shown in *(b)*.

The amplifier requires a dual rail power supply, e.g. $+/-15$ V which can be made by connecting cells as shown in figure 2.31 *(c)*. This is connected to the $+V_s$ and $-V_s$ pins.

There are two inputs to the op-amp

*(a)* the inverting input $V_-$
*(b)* the non-inverting input $V_+$.

An input signal $V_1$ at the inverting input will have its **phase** inverted, i.e. positive voltages will become negative and vice-versa, when the output is produced.

An input signal $V_2$ at the non-inverting input does not undergo a phase change in the amplifier. This is illustrated in figure 2.32.

Figure 2.32

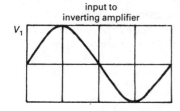

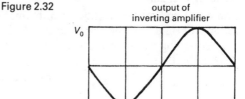

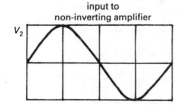

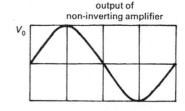

83

*Properties of an ideal op-amp*

1. **The input resistance is infinite**. This means that when connected across a voltage source there will be ideally zero current drawn from the source. It can, for example, be connected across a potential divider without affecting the output of the potential divider.

2. The op-amp will always act to ensure that the inverting and non-inverting input pins are at the same potential. **There is therefore no p.d. between the two inputs**.

### 2.8.2 The Inverting-mode Amplifier

The diagram 2.33 below shows an op-amp connected in the inverting mode.

**Figure 2.33**

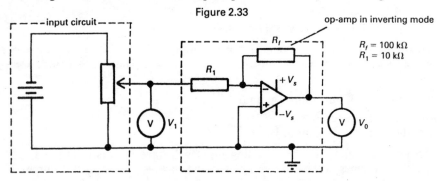

$R_f = 100 \text{ k}\Omega$
$R_1 = 10 \text{ k}\Omega$

The input circuit can either be a battery and potential divider as shown for verifying the d.c. gain, or a signal generator with variable amplitude for studying a.c. gain.

The input and output voltages can be measured using d.c. or a.c. voltmeters as appropriate. If the input p.d. $V_1$ is set at different values and the corresponding output p.d. measured, a graph of the type shown in figure 2.34 can be obtained.

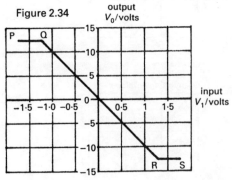

Figure 2.34

84

**Note:**

1. The gain of the amplifier can be obtained from the gradient of the graph between the points Q and R. For this circuit the gain is

$$\frac{\text{output voltage}}{\text{input voltage}} = \frac{10}{-1} = -10$$

and it is seen that this is numerically equal to the ratio

$R_f/R_1 = 100 \text{ k}\Omega/10 \text{ k}\Omega$

$R_f$ is called the **feedback resistor** as it **feeds** some of the output **back** to the input (but with an inversion of phase).

2. The voltage supply to the amplifier is +/– 15 V. This means the output of the amplifier must always be within this range. For an amplifier of gain –10, as above, an input of +1·5 V or greater will give an output of –15 V. An input p.d. of –1·5 V or more negative than –1·5 V will give an output of +15 V. This explains the flat sections PQ and RS in the graph of figure 2.34. This is caused by **saturation** of the amplifier and in practice can start at about 13·5 V for an amplifier with a supply of +/– 15 V.

3. The inversion of phase between input and output signals can also be seen from the graph, e.g. an input of 0·5 V **negative** produces an output of 5 V **positive**.

4. The effect of saturation can be used to obtain a square wave from a sinusoidal signal as shown in figure 2.35. The peak of the square wave will equal the value of the saturation voltage.

Figure 2.35

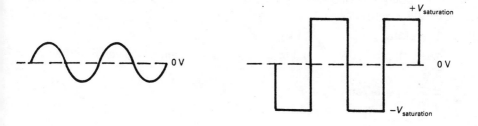

85

*Derivation of the inverting mode gain formula*

The basic circuit is shown in figure 2.36.

Figure 2.36

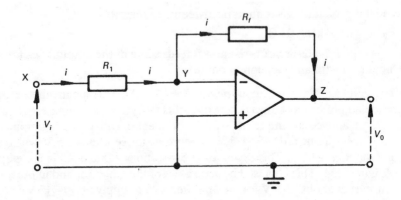

Current $i$ flows through $R_1$ and $R_f$ as shown with none (or a negligible amount) into the inverting input, because of the very high input resistance of the op-amp.

If the electron flow is as shown then point Y must be more positive than point X and point Z must be more positive than point Y.

Hence $V_Y - V_X = iR_1$ and $V_Z - V_Y = iR_f$.

Where $V_X$ is the potential at point X, $V_Y$ is the potential at Y, etc.

Also point Y must be at zero potential ($V_Y = 0$) since the non-inverting input is held at zero potential.

Therefore $-V_X = iR_i$ and $V_Z = iR_f$.

The potential at X is equal to the input p.d. $V_i$ and $V_Z$ is equal to the output p.d. $V_0$.

$\Rightarrow \ -V_i = iR_i$ and $V_0 = iR_f$

$\Rightarrow \ \dfrac{V_0}{V_i} = -\dfrac{R_f}{R_i}$

86

### 2.8.3 Differential Mode

When connected as shown in figure 2.37 the op-amp is being used in the differential mode.

Figure 2.37

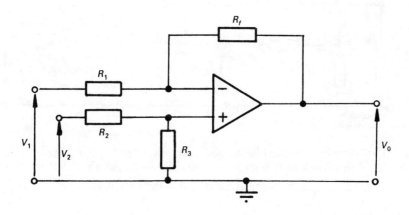

In this mode it is the **difference** between the signal applied to the non-inverting input and that applied to the inverting input which is amplified.

For the condition $\dfrac{R_1}{R_f} = \dfrac{R_2}{R_3}$

The gain equation for the differential mode is given by

$$V_0 = (V_2 - V_1)\frac{R_f}{R_i}$$

The following example should help you to understand the use of the op-amp in the differential mode to control an external device in this case a lamp.

*Example 2.6*

Figure 2.38

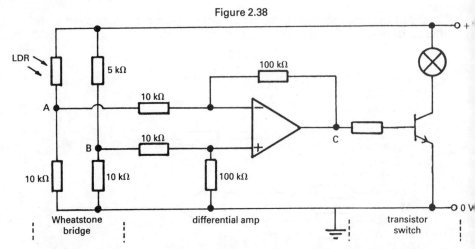

(a) Explain what happens in the above circuit when the light intensity on the LDR decreases so that its resistance increases from a value of 5 kΩ.

(b) What is the p.d. between A and B when the potential at C is 0·6 V?

Solution

(a) When the resistance of the LDR is 5 kΩ the Wheatstone bridge is balanced and the potential at A will equal the potential at B. Using the differential mode gain equation

the potential at C $= V_0 = (V_2 - V_1)\dfrac{R_f}{R_1} = (0) \times \dfrac{R_f}{R_1} = 0$.

The base is at zero potential, i.e. less than 0·6 V and the transistor is therefore like an open switch so there is no current in the lamp, and the lamp is not lit.

When the resistance of the LDR increases the bridge becomes out of balance. The out of balance p.d. is amplified by the differential amplifier and if it is of the correct sign and sufficient amplitude it will switch on the transistor.

In this case as the resistance of the LDR increases, the potential of point A decreases, i.e. $V_2 > V_1$ hence $(V_2 - V_1)$ will be positive. The potential at C will be $10 \times (V_2 - V_1)$, since $R_f/R_1$ equals 10. If this potential is greater than 0·6 V then the transistor is switched on, current flows in the lamp, and the lamp lights.

Note that a transistor is required because the op-amp cannot supply sufficient current to light the lamp.

*(b)* Using the gain equation

$$V_0 = (V_2 - V_1)\frac{R_f}{R_1}$$

$\Rightarrow \qquad 0.6 = (V_2 - V_1)\frac{100 \times 10^3}{10 \times 10^3}$

$\Rightarrow (V_2 - V_1) = 0.06$

The out-of-balance p.d. between A and B is therefore 0·06 V.

# Chapter 3

## RADIATION AND MATTER

### 3.1 CHECKLIST

**Waves and Light**

You should be able to

- [ ] 1. state that the frequency of a wave is always equal to the frequency of the source producing the wave;
- [ ] 2. state the period of a wave in terms of its frequency;
- [ ] 3. state that the energy of a wave depends on its amplitude;
- [ ] 4. explain and use correctly the terms — in phase, out of phase and coherent — as applied to waves;
- [ ] 5. explain the meaning of the terms constructive interference and destructive interference;
- [ ] 6. state that interference is the test for a wave;
- [ ] 7. state that all types of waves can be made to show reflection, refraction, diffraction and interference;
- [ ] 8. describe an experiment to demonstrate the effect of the path difference between two sources of radiation on the intensity of radiation detected at any point;
- [ ] 9. state that the condition for interference maxima and minima in an interference pattern formed by two coherent sources is given by the equation path difference $= n\lambda$ for maxima and $(n + 1/2)\lambda$ for minima where $n$ is an integer and $\lambda$ is the wavelength of the radiation;
- [ ] 10. solve problems involving the relationship in (9);
- [ ] 11. describe the effect of an optical grating on a monochromatic light beam;
- [ ] 12. solve problems using the grating equation $d \sin \theta = n\lambda$;
- [ ] 13. describe an experiment to measure the wavelength of a source of monochromatic light using a grating;
- [ ] 14. state approximate values for the wavelengths of blue, green and red light;

15. describe and compare the effects produced by a prism, and diffraction grating on a beam of
    *(a)* monochromatic light
    *(b)* white light;

16. use the following terms correctly — frequency, wavelength, monochromatic, interference, phase, amplitude, path difference, coherent, diffraction;

17. describe an experiment to show that the ratio $\dfrac{\sin \theta_1}{\sin \theta_2}$ is a constant $n$ when light passes obliquely from medium 1 to medium 2;

18. state that the absolute refractive index, $n$, of a medium is given by the ratio $\dfrac{\sin \theta_1}{\sin \theta_2}$ where $\theta_1$ is in a vacuum (or in air as an approximation) and $\theta_2$ is in the material;

19. describe a method for measuring the absolute refractive index of glass for monochromatic light;

20. solve problems involving the relationship in (18);

21. state that the refractive index of a material depends on the frequency of the light incident on the material;

22. state that the frequency of a wave does not change when it passes from one medium to another;

23. solve problems using the relationship $v = f\lambda$;

24. state the relationships $\dfrac{\sin \theta_1}{\sin \theta_2} = \dfrac{v_1}{v_2} = \dfrac{\lambda_1}{\lambda_2}$;

25. solve problems using the relationships in (24);

26. explain what is meant by total internal reflection;

27. describe an experiment to show total internal reflection;

28. explain what is meant by the critical angle $\theta_C$;

29. describe an experiment to measure the critical angle for a medium;

30. derive the relationship $\sin \theta_C = \dfrac{1}{n}$ where $\theta_C$ is the critical angle for the medium having absolute refractive index $n$;

31. solve problems involving the relationship in (30);

32. use the following terms correctly — incidence, refraction, normal, critical angle, refractive index, internal reflection.

91

**Opto-electronics**

You should be able to

1. state that the intensity $I$ of radiation striking a surface is the power per unit area of the surface;

2. state the relationship $I \propto 1/d^2$ for the intensity $I$ at a distance $d$ from a point source (an inverse square law);

3. describe a method to verify the relationship in (2);

4. state that a beam of radiation can be regarded as a stream of photons.

5. state that each photon has an energy $E = hf$ where $h$ is Planck's constant and $f$ is the frequency of the radiation;

6. solve problems involving the relationship in (5);

7. state that the intensity of radiation at any surface is $I = Nhf$ where $N$ is the number of photons per second incident per square metre of the surface;

8. describe an experiment to show
   (a) that photoemission occurs when the frequency of incident radiation is sufficiently high
   (b) the effect of intensity of radiation on photoemission;

9. explain the photoelectric effect in terms of photons;

10. describe the energy conversion taking place in the photoelectric effect in terms of the equation $E_k = hf - hf_0$ where $E_k$ is the kinetic energy of the ejected electron, $hf$ is the energy of the incident photon and $hf_0$ is the work function of the material;

11. solve problems involving the relationship in (10);

12. use the following terms correctly — photon, work function, threshold frequency, photoemission and photoelectric;

13. state that electrons in a free atom occupy discrete energy levels;

14. draw a diagram which represents the energy levels for a hydrogen atom (numbers are not required);

15. explain an emission line spectrum in terms of electron transitions between energy levels;

16. state that the photon of light in an emission line will have energy $hf$ given by $hf = W_2 - W_1$ where $W_2$ is the energy of an excited state and $W_1$ is that of a lower energy level;

☐ 17. explain an absorption line in a spectrum in terms of an electron, in a lower energy level $W_1$, absorbing photons of the correct energy $hf$ to allow it to make the transition to a higher energy level $W_2$;

☐ 18. explain the presence of absorption lines in the spectrum of sunlight;

☐ 19. use the following terms correctly — ground state, excited state, ionisation level, spectrum, emission, absorption, transition;

☐ 20. describe an experiment to display
*(a)* an emission spectrum
*(b)* an absorption spectrum;

☐ 21. describe spontaneous emission of radiation as a random process analogous to the radioactive decay of a nucleus;

☐ 22. state that an excited atom may be stimulated to emit its excess energy $hf$ if a photon of energy $hf$ is incident on it;

☐ 23. state that in stimulated emission of radiation the incident radiation and the emitted radiation
*(a)* are in phase
*(b)* travel in the same direction;

☐ 24. state that for a laser to operate the light beam must gain more energy by stimulated emission than it loses by absorption;

☐ 25. state that LASER is derived from Light Amplification by Stimulated Emission of Radiation;

☐ 26. explain the function of the two mirrors in a laser;

☐ 27. explain why a beam of laser light of $0.1$ mW may cause eye damage;

☐ 28. state that materials may be classified as conductors, insulators or semiconductors according to their electrical properties;

☐ 29. give examples of conductors, insulators and semiconductors;

☐ 30. state that doping is the process of adding impurity atoms to a pure semiconductor;

☐ 31. state that the resistance of a pure semiconductor decreases by doping;

☐ 32. explain the formation of
*(a)* *n*-type semiconductors
*(b)* *p*-type semiconductors;

☐ 33. describe the movement of charge carriers in
*(a)* a forward biased *pn*-junction diode
*(b)* a reverse biased *pn*-junction diode;

34. explain the operation of an LED in terms of the recombination of positive and negative charge carriers;

35. state that in a solid-state photodiode positive and negative charges are produced by light incident on the *p-n* junction;

36. state that a photodiode used in the photovoltaic mode may be used to supply electrical power to a load;

37. state that a photodiode may be used in the photoconductive mode as a light sensor;

38. state that in a photodiode the reverse leakage current is
    (a) directly proportional to the intensity of light
    (b) independent of the reverse biasing voltage (if this is below the breakdown voltage);

39. state that a photodiode has a very fast switching action.

## Radioactivity

You should be able to

1. describe how Rutherford showed that
   (a) compared to the atom, the nucleus has a relatively small diameter
   (b) most of the mass of the atom is concentrated in the nucleus;

2. state that a nucleus contains protons and neutrons and has a net positive charge;

3. explain what is meant by alpha, beta and gamma decay;

4. use and interpret symbols of the form $^4_2$He, $^0_{-1}$e, $^1_0$n;

5. identify the processes occurring in nuclear reactions described using symbols of the type given in (4);

6. define the average activity $A$ of a quantity of radioactive substance by the relationship $A = N/t$ where $N$ is the number of nuclei decaying in time $t$;

7. state that the becquerel is the unit of activity and that one becquerel is one decay per second;

8. solve problems using the relationship in (6);

9. define the absorbed dose $D$ as the energy absorbed per unit mass of the absorbing material;

10. state that the gray (Gy) is the unit of absorbed dose and that one gray is one joule per kilogram;

11. explain the use of the quality factor $Q$ of each kind of radiation as a measure of its biological effect;

☐ 12. define the dose equivalent $H$ from the relationship $H = D \times Q$;

☐ 13. state that the unit of dose equivalent is the sievert (Sv);

☐ 14. solve problems involving the relationship in (12);

☐ 15. define the dose equivalent rate $= H/t$;

☐ 16. give typical background dose equivalent rates in mSv per year or μSv per hour;

☐ 17. give examples of the factors affecting background radiation level (2·0 mSv per year);

☐ 18. state that upper limits have been set for exposure
   *(a)* to the general public (5 mSv, above background, in any year)
   *(b)* workers exposed as part of their employment (50 mSv, above background, in any year);

☐ 19. describe an experiment to show how the intensity of a beam of gamma radiation varies with thickness of an absorber and how the results are used to calculate the half-value thickness;

☐ 20. sketch a graph to show the variation of intensity of a beam of gamma radiation with thickness of absorber;

☐ 21. solve problems involving half-value thicknesses;

☐ 22. state that the dose equivalent rate is reduced by
   *(a)* shielding
   *(b)* increasing the distance from the source;

☐ 23. describe fission as the process whereby a nucleus of large mass number splits into two nuclei of smaller mass numbers along with several neutrons;

☐ 24. state that fission may be *(a)* spontaneous or *(b)* induced by neutron bombardment;

☐ 25. describe fusion as the process whereby two nuclei combine to form a nucleus of larger mass number;

☐ 26. explain using $E = mc^2$, how the products resulting from a fission or fusion process gain large amounts of kinetic energy;

☐ 27. use the following terms correctly in context — nucleon, nuclide, isotope, atomic number, mass number, radioisotope (radionuclide) nuclear fission, nuclear fusion, mass defect.

## 3.2 PHYSICAL QUANTITIES AND UNITS

| Quantity | Quantity Symbol | Unit Symbol | Unit |
|---|---|---|---|
| **Radiation** | | | |
| wavelength | $\lambda$ | m | metre |
| frequency | $f$ | Hz | hertz |
| speed of light in vacuo | $c$ | m s$^{-1}$ | metre per second |
| refractive index | $n$ | no unit | no unit |
| critical angle | $\theta_C$, $i_C$ | $^\circ$ | degree |
| intensity of light | $I$ | W m$^{-2}$ | watt per square metre |
| Planck's constant | $h$ | J s | joule second |
| work function | $W$ | J | joule |
| **Radioactivity** | | | |
| proton number | $Z$ | | |
| mass number | $A$ | | |
| activity number | $A$ | Bq | becquerel |
| absorbed dose | $D$ | Gy | gray, joule per kg |
| quality factor | $Q$ | | |
| dose equivalent | $H$ | Sv | sievert |
| dose equivalent rate | $\dot{H}$ | Sv h$^{-1}$<br>Sv yr$^{-1}$ | sievert per hour<br>sievert per year |
| absorbed dose rate | $\dot{D}$ | Gy h$^{-1}$<br>Gy yr$^{-1}$ | gray per hour<br>gray per year |

### 3.3 FORMULAE

**Radiation**

1. Period $T = \dfrac{1}{f}$

2. Speed of a wave $v = f\lambda$

3. Optical path difference for maxima $= n\lambda$
   $\qquad\qquad\qquad$ for minima $= \left(n + \dfrac{1}{2}\right)\lambda$ where $n$ is integer

4. Grating equation $d \sin\theta = n\lambda$

5. Absolute refractive index $n = \dfrac{\sin i}{\sin r}$

   $i$ is angle of incidence in vacuum, $r$ is angle of refraction in material

6. $n_1 \sin\theta_1 = n_2 \sin\theta_2$

7. $\dfrac{\sin\theta_1}{\sin\theta_2} = \dfrac{v_1}{v_2} = \dfrac{\lambda_1}{\lambda_2}$

8. $\sin i_C = \dfrac{1}{n}$

9. Intensity $I \propto \dfrac{1}{d^2}$

10. Energy of one photon $= hf$ where $h$ is Planck's constant and $f$ is the frequency of the radiation

11. Intensity of radiation $I = Nhf$ where $N$ is number of photons per second

12. Work function $W = hf_0$ where $f_0$ is the threshold frequency

13. Photoelectric effect $hf = W + 1/2\ mv^2$
    $$E_k = hf - hf_0$$

14. Energy of emitted photon $hf = W_2 - W_1$ where $W_2 > W_1$

**Radioactivity**

15. Activity $A = \dfrac{N}{t}$ where $N$ is the number of nuclei decaying in time $t$.

16. Dose equivalent $= H = DQ$ where $Q$ is the quality factor and $D$ the absorbed dose.

17. Dose equivalent rate $= \dot{H} = \dfrac{H}{t}$

18. $E = m c^2$

D

## 3.4 WAVES AND LIGHT

### 3.4.1 Wave properties

Waves carry energy and the energy of a wave increases as the **amplitude** of the wave increases. The amplitude of a wave is ½ of the distance between the "crest" and the "trough" of the wave.

The frequency of a wave is equal to the frequency of the source which produces the wave (the exception, which is not in this course, is when the source is moving). The frequency **does not depend** on the amplitude of the wave from the source. You can check this with sound waves. Listen to a note from a tape-recorder and verify that the frequency does not change as you alter the setting of the volume control. Also once the wave has left the source its frequency will remain constant.

You should already be familiar with some of the ways in which waves behave, such as

(i) **reflection** from an obstacle, such that the angle of incidence equals the angle of reflection;

(ii) **refraction** when a wave passes from one medium to another resulting in a change in direction (unless it enters along the normal to the boundary);

(iii) **diffraction** when a wave bends around an obstacle (a wave with a long wavelength diffracts more than one with a shorter wavelength).

If we are trying to prove that energy is being transmitted as a wave then the above behaviour is not sufficient proof. We must look for **interference**.

### 3.4.2 Interference

What is interference and what are the necessary conditions for interference to occur?

Interference of waves occurs when waves, under certain conditions, meet each other. For interference to occur the waves must be **coherent**, i.e. have a constant phase difference between them. This implies that the waves have the same frequency, speed and wavelength.

Figure 3.1

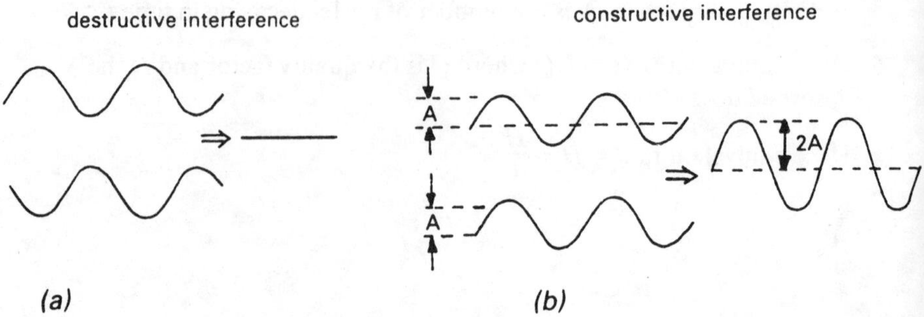

destructive interference

constructive interference

(a)                              (b)

98

In figure 3.1 *(a)* the two waves of equal amplitude have a constant phase difference of 180°, i.e. are completely out of phase. When the interference takes place they cancel each other out; **destructive interference**.

Figure 3.1 *(b)* shows two waves, of amplitude A, meeting with a constant phase difference of 0°, i.e. in phase. The waves interfere at this meeting point to give a wave of resultant amplitude 2A; **constructive interference**.

The above obviously does not happen when solid objects meet — hence the test for a wave.

*Examples of Interference*

The examples given in figure 3.2 are for a microwave source but the effects can be reproduced for light using the appropriate apparatus.

Figure 3.2

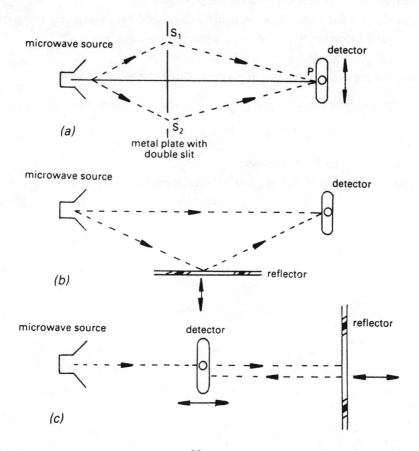

99

In each of the three experiments interference occurs at the position of the detector because the waves arrive at the detector by two different paths from the source.

The Young's double slit apparatus in (a) allows light to arrive from the two slits $S_1$ and $S_2$ which act as coherent sources.

In (b) the waves arrive at the detector either directly from the source or after reflection from the metal reflector.

At the detector in (c); the interference is between waves arriving directly from the source and those which have passed earlier and have been reflected from the metal reflector.

The difference in path lengths for the two possible routes taken by the waves can be changed by moving the detector in (a), the reflector in (b) and the reflector and/or detector in (c). The phase difference between waves on arrival at the detector depends on this path difference.

For constructive interference in figure 3.2 (a) producing maxima of intensity

path difference $S_1P - S_2P = n\lambda$ where $n$ is an integer

i.e. path difference $\quad = 0, \lambda, 2\lambda$, etc.

For destructive interference in (a) producing minima of intensity

path difference $S_1P - S_2P = \left(n + \frac{1}{2}\right)\lambda$ where $n$ is an integer

$$= \frac{1}{2}\lambda, \frac{3}{2}\lambda, \text{ etc}$$

*Young's Double Slit Experiment*

The simplest way of showing interference of light is shown below.

Figure 3.3

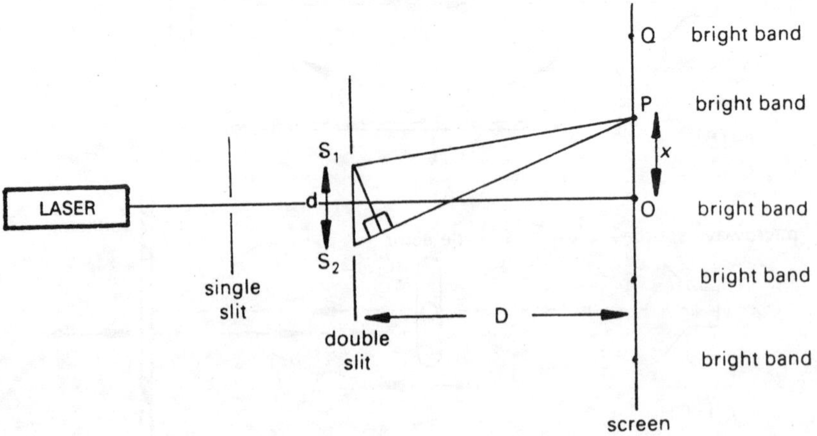

In figure 3.3 the light beam from a laser, monochromatic source, is directed at two narrow slits which have been formed on a blackened slide. The slits are usually about 0·2 mm apart. A bright band or maximum of intensity occurs at O on the screen because the path lengths $S_1O$ and $S_2O$ are equal. If P is the position of the closest bright band (first maximum) to O then $S_2P - S_1P = \lambda$.

This path difference is shown by $\Delta$ in the diagram.

The next maximum will occur at Q if $S_2Q - S_1Q = 2\lambda$.

## Diffraction grating

We have seen above how an interference pattern can be produced using two narrow slits. The effect is much stronger if we increase the number of slits. A **diffraction grating** is a set of parallel equidistant slits cut into glass or on a cheaper plastic copy. There may be 500 lines or slits per 1 mm of the grating, i.e. a slit separation of $2 \times 10^{-6}$ m. Each slit acts as a source of coherent waves.

If a grating is used in place of the double slit in figure 3.3 the pattern of interference maxima and minima is the same but the maxima are much narrower and hence brighter.

The grating equation can be defined with the aid of figure 3.4.

Figure 3.4

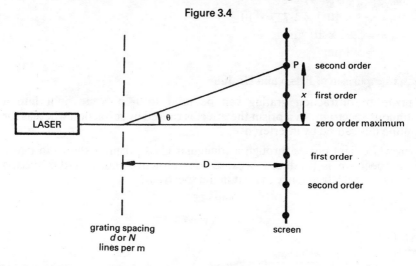

The interference pattern is symmetric about the central or zero order maximum. The condition for a maximum of intensity is given by $n\lambda = d \sin \theta$, where $n$ is the order of the maximum, and $d$ is the slit separation. Note that it is usual to quote $N$ the number of lines per millimetre or metre of the grating. $d = \frac{1}{N}$ with appropriate units.

Note that for the distances involved in this experiment, $\sin \theta$ is approximately equal to $\frac{x}{D}$.

This experiment can be used to measure the wavelength of the light from the laser as in the example below.

*Example 3.1*

In an experiment using the apparatus as in figure 3.4 the distance between the central maximum and the 4th order maximum is found to be 94·5 mm. The distance between the screen and the grating is 2·000 m and the grating has 20 lines per mm.

Calculate the wavelength of the light used.

Solution:

$$\sin \theta = \frac{x}{D} = \frac{94{\cdot}5 \times 10^{-3}}{2} = 4{\cdot}725 \times 10^{-2}$$

$N = 20$ lines per mm $= 20 \times 10^3$ lines per m

$$d = \frac{1}{N} = \frac{1}{20 \times 10^3} = 5 \times 10^{-5} \text{ m}$$

Using $n\lambda = d \sin \theta$

$$4\lambda = 5 \times 10^{-5} \times 4{\cdot}725 \times 10^{-2}$$
$$\lambda = 5{\cdot}91 \times 10^{-7} \text{ m}$$
$$= 591 \text{ nm}$$

### 3.4.3 Comparison of Prism and Grating

A prism or diffraction grating can be used to split white light into a continuous spectrum. In a prism the effect is caused by refraction whereas for a grating it is caused by interference.

When white light passes through a triangular glass prism as shown in figure 3.5, a spectrum is produced because the refractive index of the glass is different for each frequency of light in the spectrum.

Figure 3.5

PRISM

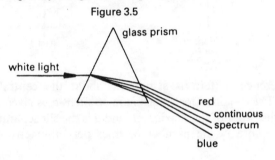

102

**Note:**

When a prism is used:

1. only a single spectrum is observed
2. blue light is refracted through a greater angle than red light.

The grating is usually used with a **spectrometer** as in figure 3.6 (a) which enables the angle θ to be measured for a particular wavelength of light and order of spectrum.

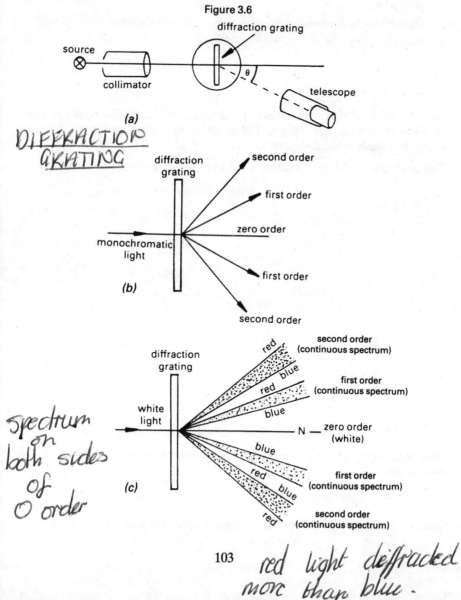

Figure 3.6

DIFFRACTION GRATING

*spectrum on both sides of O order*

103

*red light diffracted more than blue.*

Figure 3.6 (b) and (c) show the interference effects obtained using a monochromatic (b) and a white light (c) source.

**Note:**

When a diffraction grating is used:

1. the spectrum is repeated several times
2. for a particular order, the angle $\theta$ for blue light is smaller than the angle $\theta$ for red light
3. the central or zero order fringe is always the same colour as the source
4. there is always an odd number of fringes.

### 3.4.4 Refraction

Bending or **refraction** of light takes place when light passes from one medium to another, e.g. air into glass. The bending is caused by the light having different speeds in the different media.

The apparatus of figure 3.7 can be used to investigate refraction.

Figure 3.7

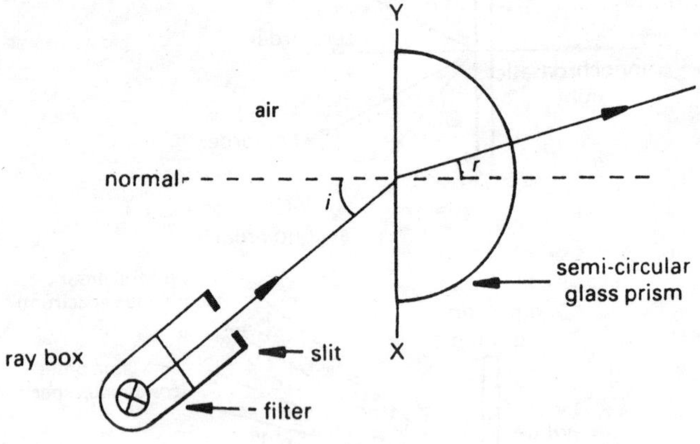

$i$ = angle of incidence    $r$ = angle of refraction

The angle of refraction $r$ is measured for different angles of incidence $i$. The results show:

$$\frac{\sin i}{\sin r} = \text{constant} = n$$

which is Snell's law where $n$ is the refractive index (of glass in this case).

104

Strictly, the refractive index $n$ of a medium is the ratio $\sin i / \sin r$ when the light is entering the medium **from** a vacuum. The approximation made in this experiment where light passes from air into glass is a small one at this level.

Figure 3.8

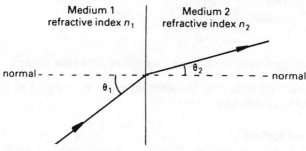

For light travelling from medium 1 of refractive index $n_1$ into medium 2 of refractive index $n_2$, as in figure 3.8, Snell's law can be applied in the form:

$$n_1 \sin \theta_1 = n_2 \sin \theta_2$$

**Note:**

(i) Angles are measured between the rays and the normal to the surface.

(ii) If $n_1 < n_2$ then $\theta_1 > \theta_2$ and the ray changes direction towards the normal on refraction, e.g. as in air to glass.

(iii) If $n_1 > n_2$ then $\theta_1 < \theta_2$ and the ray moves away from the normal on refraction, e.g. glass into air.

(iv) The ray directions are reversible, e.g. changing the arrow directions in figure 3.8. illustrates light travelling from medium 2 into medium 1.

Now an example to illustrate how easy it is to apply this relationship.

*Example 3.2*

Light travels from glass (refractive index 1.5) into air (refractive index 1.0) as shown in figure 3.9

Figure 3.9

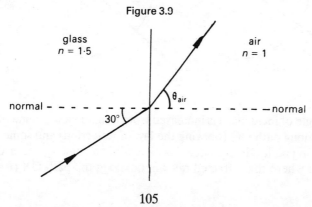

Solution:

Ensure that any angles given are between rays and normals.

$$n_{glass} \sin \theta_{glass} = n_{air} \sin \theta_{air}$$
$$\Rightarrow \quad 1 \cdot 5 \sin 30° = 1 \sin \theta_{air}$$
$$\Rightarrow \quad \sin \theta_{air} = 0 \cdot 75$$
$$\Rightarrow \quad \theta_{air} = 48 \cdot 6°$$

The light emerges from the glass at an angle of 49° to the normal.

In any problem on refraction the formula $n_1 \sin \theta_1 = n_2 \sin \theta_2$ is used at the interface between different media.

**Total Internal Reflection**

Total internal reflection, as the wording implies, is when reflection takes place at the internal surface of a medium and no light emerges from that medium.

The apparatus of figure 3.10 (a) can be used to observe the effect of a ray of light striking the plane surface XOY of a semicircular glass block.

Figure 3.10

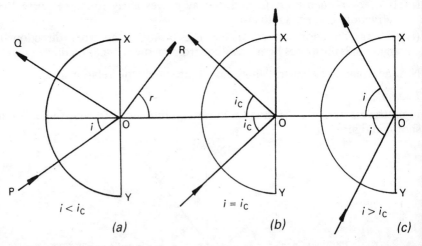

As the angle of incidence $i$ is increased from a small value, some of the light is **reflected** along path OQ (obeying the law of reflection) and some is **refracted** to pass along path OR. As angle $i$ is increased an angle $i_c$, the **critical angle $i_c$** is reached where the refracted ray will be along the path OX ($r = 90°$) as in

106

figure (b). If $i$ is increased further $(i > i_c)$ as in diagram (c) **all** the light is reflected from the surface XOY. This is **total internal reflection**. The value of $i_c$ for a particular material can be calculated from its refractive index.

$$n_{glass} \sin \theta_{glass} = n_{air} \sin \theta_{air}$$

The angle of refraction is 90° when the angle of incidence is the critical angle $i_c$

$$\Rightarrow \quad n_{glass} \sin i_c = 1 \sin 90°$$

$$\Rightarrow \quad \sin i_c = 1/n_{glass}$$

Note that total internal reflection can only occur when light travels from one medium towards another having a lower refractive index than the first.

*Example 3.3*

Calculate the path taken by a ray of light XY entering a triangular prism, as shown in figure 3.11, where the refractive index of glass is 1·5.

**Figure 3.11**

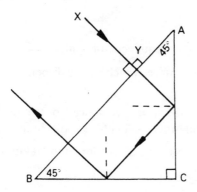

Solution:

The ray passes through surface AB without change in direction because it enters along the normal to the surface. It strikes surface AC at an angle of 45° to the normal. The critical angle is given by $\sin i_c = \dfrac{1}{1·5}$ hence $i_c = 41·8°$. There is therefore total internal reflection at surface AC and similarly at surface BC. The light follows the path shown to leave parallel to the incident ray.

## Effect of refraction on speed and wavelength

For light of one frequency (monochromatic) passing from vacuum (or air to a good approximation) into a different medium, say glass, as in figure 3.12 the refractive index can be defined in terms of angles of incidence and refraction.

Figure 3.12

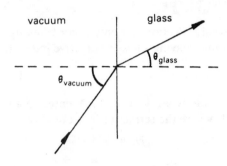

$$\text{Refractive index} = n_{\text{glass}} = \frac{\sin \theta_{\text{vacuum}}}{\sin \theta_{\text{glass}}}$$

$n_{\text{glass}}$ is different for different frequencies of light.

It is the differing refractive indices which causes dispersion of white light by a prism to cause a spectrum.

In wave optics the ratio of the refractive indices for two media can be related to the speeds and wavelengths of the light (or wave) in the media.

Many standard textbooks contain a derivation of the relationship

$$\frac{\sin \theta_{\text{vacuum}}}{\sin \theta_{\text{glass}}} = \frac{\lambda_{\text{vacuum}}}{\lambda_{\text{glass}}}$$

for light being refracted as in figure 3.12. The proof is lengthy but worth studying although it is not required for the examination.

From the wave equation $c = f\lambda_{\text{vacuum}}$ where $c$ is the speed in a vacuum,

$$\text{and } v_{\text{glass}} = f\lambda_{\text{glass}}$$

Note that the **frequency of the light is the same in the glass as it was in the vacuum**.

$$\text{then } n_{\text{glass}} = \frac{\sin \theta_{\text{vacuum}}}{\sin \theta_{\text{glass}}} = \frac{\lambda_{\text{vacuum}}}{\lambda_{\text{glass}}} = \frac{c}{v_{\text{glass}}}$$

For two media of refractive index $n_1$ and $n_2$

$$\frac{n_2}{n_1} = \frac{c/v_2}{c/v_1} = \frac{v_1}{v_2} \quad \text{where } v_1 \text{ is the speed of light in medium 1, etc.}$$

Combining all the above relationships gives

$$\frac{n_2}{n_1} = \frac{v_1}{v_2} = \frac{\lambda_1}{\lambda_2} = \frac{\sin \theta_1}{\sin \theta_2}$$

**Note:**

1. The velocity of light is greatest in vacuum hence $c > v$ and refractive indices will have values greater than 1.
2. A material with a high refractive index is more optically dense than a material with a lower refractive index.

### Example 3.4

Monochromatic light of wavelength $5 \cdot 0 \times 10^{-7}$ m in air travels from air into glass of refractive index 1·5. What is (a) the speed of light in the glass and (b) the wavelength of the light in glass.

Solution:

(a) $\quad \dfrac{n_{\text{glass}}}{n_{\text{air}}} = \dfrac{\text{speed in air}}{\text{speed in glass}}$

$\Rightarrow \quad \dfrac{1 \cdot 5}{1} = \dfrac{3 \cdot 0 \times 10^8}{v_{\text{glass}}}$

$\Rightarrow \quad v_{\text{glass}} = 2 \times 10^8 \text{ m s}^{-1}$

(b) Use $\dfrac{n_{\text{glass}}}{n_{\text{air}}} = \dfrac{\lambda_{\text{air}}}{\lambda_{\text{glass}}}$ to obtain $\lambda_{\text{glass}} = 3 \cdot 3 \times 10^{-7}$ m

or $\quad\quad v_{\text{air}} = f \lambda_{\text{air}}$

$\Rightarrow \quad 3 \cdot 0 \times 10^8 = f \times 5 \times 10^{-7}$

$\Rightarrow \quad\quad\quad f = 6 \times 10^{14} \text{ Hz}$

Since $\quad f_{\text{air}} = f_{\text{glass}}$

$\quad\quad\quad v_{\text{glass}} = f \lambda_{\text{glass}}$

$\Rightarrow \quad 2 \times 10^8 = 6 \times 10^{14} \times \lambda_{\text{glass}}$

$\Rightarrow \quad\quad \lambda_{\text{glass}} = 3 \cdot 3 \times 10^{-7} \text{ m}$

## 3.5   OPTO-ELECTRONICS

### 3.5.1  Intensity of Light

The intensity of light at a point is the power per unit area of surface (unit is $W\,m^{-2}$).

The apparatus of figure 3.13 can be used to establish the relationship between the intensity $I$ of light and the distance $r$ from the point source of light. The equipment consists of a small lamp (point source), a light level meter and a metre rule.

Figure 3.13

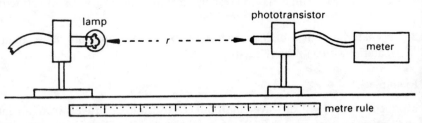

Measurements of light intensity are made at different distances $r$ from the lamp. The results show that the intensity of light **decreases** as the distance of the point from the source **increases**.

A graph of $I$ against $1/r^2$ is a straight line showing that

$$\text{Intensity of light} \quad I \propto \frac{1}{r^2} \quad \text{or} \quad \text{Intensity} = \frac{k}{r^2} \text{ where } k \text{ is a constant.}$$

This relationship can be understood by considering the situation of figure 3.14.

Figure 3.14

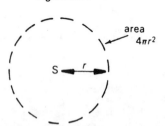

The point source sends light out symmetrically so that all points on the sphere of radius $r$ will have the same intensity of light. If the power of the source is $P$ then the total power at the sphere is also $P$ and the intensity $I = P/(4\pi r^2)$. Hence $I = k/r^2$. Any sphere with a different radius will have the same total power through its surface.

### 3.5.2 The Photoelectric Effect

The photoelectric effect provides evidence for the model of light as quanta of energy or photons. A beam of radiation is regarded as a stream of quanta of energy called photons. Each photon has an energy $E = hf$ where $f$ is the frequency of the radiation and $h$ is Planck's constant equal to $6.63 \times 10^{-34}$ J s.

In a metal there are some electrons, conduction electrons, which are free to move under the action of electric or magnetic fields. The work function $W$ for a particular metal is the minimum quantum of energy which must be supplied to emit an electron from the surface of the metal. In the photoelectric effect this is supplied in the form of photons of light.

Figure 3.15

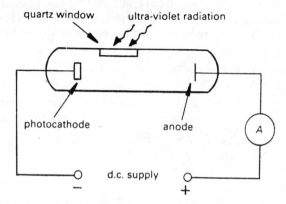

Figure 3.15 shows an experimental arrangement to investigate the emission of electrons from a metal as the frequency and intensity of the incident light are varied. The emission of electrons from the **photocathode** results in a current in the external circuit. The graphs in figure 3.16 (a) and (b) show the typical results of the experiment.

Figure 3.16

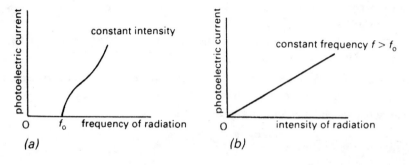

**Note:**

1. Graph (a) indicates that no emission takes place until radiation with a frequency greater than a critical, or threshold frequency $f_o$ is used. The value of $f_o$ depends on the metal used for the photocathode.

2. Graph (a) is consistent with the model that light of frequency $f$ is composed of quanta each of energy $hf$. When $hf < W$ there is insufficient energy to cause electron emission. When $hf > W$ then emission of electrons takes place. At the threshold frequency $hf_o = W$.

3. It is not possible for two or more photons each of frequency less than $f_o$ to act together and cause photoelectric emission.

4. The number of photons in the incident light is directly proportional to the intensity of the source. Graph (b) confirms that one photon can only act on one electron as there is direct proportionality between number of electrons emitted per second, i.e. the current, and the intensity of the incident light.

5. When the photon has energy $hf > W$ the emitted photon has kinetic energy $(\frac{1}{2}mv^2)$.

Energy of photon = Energy to overcome + kinetic energy of
work function      emitted electrons

$\Rightarrow$                 $hf = W + \frac{1}{2}mv^2$

$\Rightarrow$                 $hf = hf_o + \frac{1}{2}mv^2$

*Example 3.5*

A metal has a work function equal to $6 \cdot 0 \times 10^{-19}$ J. Will radiation of frequency $1 \cdot 5 \times 10^{15}$ Hz cause photoelectric emission in this metal?

Solution:

Energy of incoming photon = $hf$

$= 6 \cdot 63 \times 10^{-34} \times 1 \cdot 5 \times 10^{15}$

$= 9 \cdot 9 \times 10^{-19}$ J

This energy is greater than the work function of the metal hence photoelectric emission will take place.

Electrons with a maximum kinetic energy of $(9 \cdot 9 \times 10^{-19} - 6 \times 10^{-19})$ J will be emitted from the metal.

Note that if the number of photons striking 1 m$^2$ of a surface every second is $N$ and the energy of each photon is $hf$ then

energy per second incident on surface = $Nhf$

$\Rightarrow$    intensity $I = Nhf$

### 3.5.3 The Model of the Atom

The **simple** model of the atom has the following characteristics:

1. At the centre of the atom there is a positively charged nucleus which contributes most of the atomic mass.

2. The nucleus is surrounded by a cloud of electrons whose total negative charge equals the positive charge on the nucleus.

3. Electric charge is always an integral multiple of $1.6 \times 10^{-19}$ C, the charge of a single electron.

4. The electrons can have only certain permitted energies in the atom and these are unique to the type of atom. These energies are represented by **energy level** diagrams such as in figure 3.17 which represents the energy levels for a hydrogen atom. The lowest of these levels is the **ground state**.

Figure 3.17

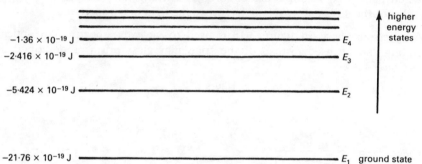

5. If the atom is given a **precise** appropriate amount of energy an electron can move from a lower level to a higher level, e.g. $E_1$ to $E_3$ and is then in an **excited state** The amount of energy required for this **transition** is $(E_3 - E_1)$ and is an energy packet or **quantum** of energy.

6. An electron in an excited state can "drop" to a lower energy level releasing a quantum of energy of electromagnetic radiation of frequency $f$. A quantum of light is called a **photon**.

7. The energy of the emitted photon is equal to the change in energy of the electron during the transition, e.g. $E_3 - E_2$.

8. The energy $E$ of a photon of the emitted radiation is given by $E = hf$ where $h$ is Planck's constant equal to $6.63 \times 10^{-34}$ J s.

9. If an electron is removed from its normal energy level to infinity, the atom is then in an **ionisation state**.

113

E

*Example 3.4*

For the electron transition $E_3$ to $E_2$ in figure 3.17 calculate *(a)* the energy of the photon emitted and *(b)* the frequency of the radiation emitted.

Solution:

*(a)* Energy of photon = Energy difference between levels $E_3$ and $E_2$

$$= 3{\cdot}008 \times 10^{-19} \text{ J}$$

*(b)* Energy of photon = $hf$

$$\Rightarrow 3{\cdot}008 \times 10^{-19} = 6{\cdot}63 \times 10^{-34} \times f$$

Frequency $f$ of radiation = $4{\cdot}53 \times 10^{14}$ Hz

This emitted radiation is in the red range of visible light.

### 3.5.4 Spectra

When light from a source passes through a triangular glass prism the light paths for the different wavelengths spread the light into a **spectrum**.

A **spectrometer** as in figure 3.18 is used to view the spectra. An optical grating can be used instead of the triangular glass prism as described in section 3.4.3.

Figure 3.18

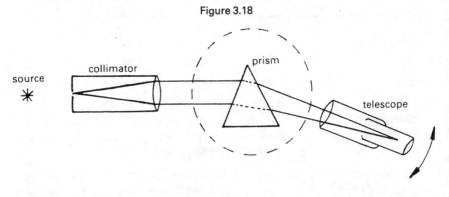

There are two basic types of spectra namely emission and absorption. Each of these types is further subdivided.

### (A) EMISSION SPECTRA

Optical emission spectra are the distributions of frequencies of light obtained from elements and compounds when the electrons in the elements or compounds, in vapour form, have been given additional energy by heating or applying a strong electric field to them.

114

1. *Continuous Emission Spectra* — in which all the wavelengths of visible light are present, see figure 3.19 (a).

Figure 3.19

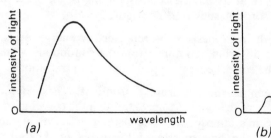 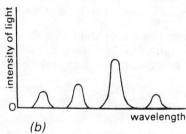

(a)

(b)

This is produced by the white light from a tungsten lamp.

2. *Line Emission Spectra* — these consist of a series of coloured lines on a dark background, see figure 3.19 (b). Line spectra are produced by electrical discharge lamps containing vapour of elements such as sodium, mercury, cadmium, etc. Each element emits its unique set of spectral lines which can be used to identify it. This uniqueness is consistent with the existence of distinct energy levels for electrons in atoms of a specific element. The intensity of a particular spectral line depends on the probability of the related electron transition taking place.

(B) ABSORPTION SPECTRA

Each element can absorb radiation of the same discrete frequencies as it emits.

Figure 3.20

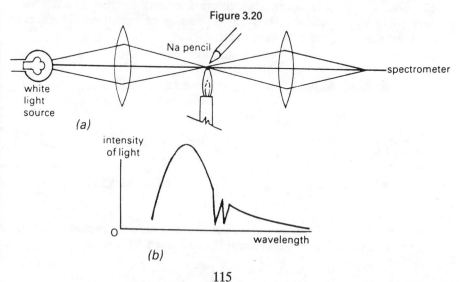

(a)

(b)

115

In figure 3.20 (a) white light is focussed in the region where sodium vapour is being formed by the sodium pencil in the bunsen flame. At the spectrometer a spectrum composed of dark lines on a background of a continuous spectrum is observed. The dark lines are at frequencies corresponding to the spectral lines of sodium. This is an absorption spectrum, see figure 3.20 (b).

Again this is consistent with the hypothesis of discrete electron energy levels. The atoms in the vapour are absorbing photons, from the continuous white light spectrum, which have the correct energy to permit electron transitions.

Absorption lines can be seen in the spectrum of sunlight. These occur because the light from the core of the sun has to pass through the cooler gases in the outer layers of the Sun's atmosphere. The dark lines occur at the frequencies corresponding to the line spectra of the gases in the Sun's atmosphere.

### 3.5.5 Lasers

The transition of an electron from a higher energy level to a lower energy level with the emission of a photon can either be

(a) **spontaneous**, i.e. a random process similar to the radioactive decay of a nucleus,

or

(b) **stimulated**, i.e. the transition is triggered by a photon of energy $hf$ equal to the energy transition of the electron.

In **stimulated emission** of a photon the emitted photon is always in **phase** with the photon which triggered the process and both photons travel in the same direction. It is these properties which are necessary for the operation of a **laser** (light amplification by stimulated emission of radiation). The energy level diagrams in figure 3.21 illustrate the process.

Figure 3.21

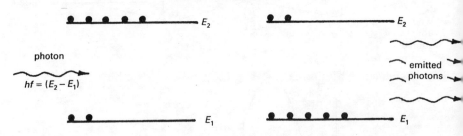

For laser action to take place there must be a **population inversion**, i.e. a high energy state which has more electrons than a lower energy state.

Laser action can be obtained in a helium-neon gas mixture. The gas mixture is enclosed in a quartz tube which is positioned between two mirrors as in figure 3.22.

**Figure 3.22**

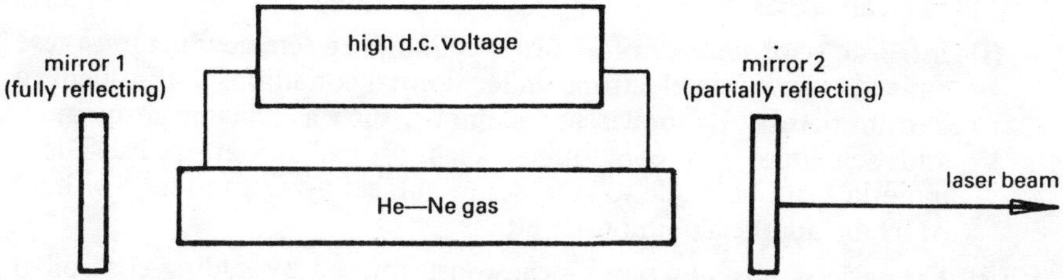

Helium atoms are excited to higher energy states by collisions with ions in the gas mixture. Energy is then passed from the helium atoms to the neon atoms. As electrons in the neon make the transition to a lower energy level photons of light are emitted. Most of this light is trapped in the gas mixture as a result of being reflected by the two mirrors. The conditions are such that the light beam gains more energy (photons) by stimulated emission than it loses by absorption. The **partially silvered** mirror allows a small fraction of the light beam to escape to form the laser beam.

Light from a laser

*(a)* is monochromatic
*(b)* is coherent (all photons in phase)
*(c)* is intense because of the coherence
*(d)* forms a parallel beam because of the plane parallel mirrors.

Because the beam is intense and parallel it is a potential hazard to the eye. A laser of power 0·10 mW forming a beam of radius 0·50 mm produces a light intensity given by

$$\text{light intensity} = \frac{\text{power}}{\text{area}} = \frac{0\cdot1 \times 10^{-3}}{\pi r^2} = \frac{0\cdot1 \times 10^{-3}}{\pi \times (0\cdot5 \times 10^{-3})^2} = 127$$

This gives a light intensity of 127 W m$^{-2}$ which can cause eye damage.

### 3.5.6 Conductors, Semiconductors and Insulators

Materials can be divided into **three** broad categories according to their electrical properties.

*(a)* **Conductors** — these have many free electrons which can be moved by an electric field applied across the material. Examples of conductors are — metals, graphite, antimony and arsenic.

117

(b) **Insulators** — these materials have too few free electrons to allow conduction. Examples are paper, wood and rubber.

(c) **Semiconductors** — are a class of materials which all conduct electricity better with increasing temperature. We can further divide these materials into two categories.

   (i) **Intrinsic semiconductors** — often called **pure semiconductors**, these have very few free electrons under normal conditions and so behave like insulators. Examples are elements such as silicon, germanium and selenium and compounds such as gallium arsenide. These materials can be made to conduct by subjecting them to heat or light or by the addition of impurity atoms.

   (ii) **Extrinsic semiconductors** — these are formed by adding controlled amounts of "impurity" atoms to a pure or intrinsic semiconductor. This process is called **"doping"**. The effect of this doping is to increase the number of **charge carriers** and hence decrease the resistance compared to the pure semiconductor.

### Energy band diagrams

Energy band diagrams such as those in figure 3.23 are used to explain the electrical properties of materials.

Figure 3.23

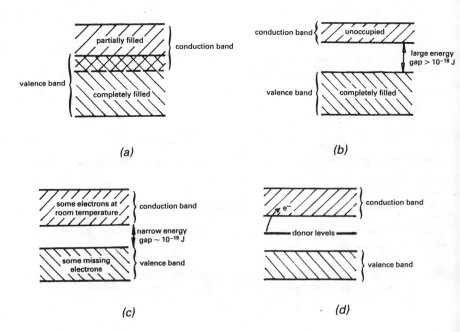

118

There are basically two energy bands in this model, the valence band and the conduction band. Electrons in the valence band are attached to individual atoms while those in the conduction band are **free** to move throughout the material. Electrons in a material fill the bands from the lowest level at the bottom of the valence band upwards.

In a **metal**, figure 3.23 (a), the valence band is completely filled and the conduction band is partially filled. Electrical conduction can therefore take place.

In an **insulator**, figure 3.23 (b), there are no free electrons in the conduction band. Also the energy gap between the two bands is too large for electrons to jump between the two bands. Hence electrical conduction cannot take place.

In an **intrinsic semiconductor**, figure 3.23 (c), the energy gap is smaller than for an insulator. If the temperature is increased then electrons in the valence band gain energy and move to the conduction band; hence allowing conduction to take place.

When a pure semiconductor is doped by adding impurity atoms an energy level is created between the conduction and valence bands, see figure 3.23 (d). In the example shown, electrons from the impurity atoms occupy this "donor" level and can easily gain sufficient energy to jump into the conduction band.

### N-type and p-type semiconductors

There are two basic types of extrinsic semiconductors, i.e. n-type and p-type. These are formed depending on the type of impurity atoms used to dope the pure semiconductor. In an **n-type** semiconductor the majority of the charge carriers for conduction are **electrons**. In **p-type** the marjority of carriers are **positive**. To understand their behaviour we must look at the crystal lattice of the materials.

Silicon has a valence of four. This means it can be regarded as a positive core (consisting of its nucleus and tightly bound electrons) along with four valence electrons which can be shared. These valence electrons enable the atom to link with others as shown in figure 3.24 (a).

119

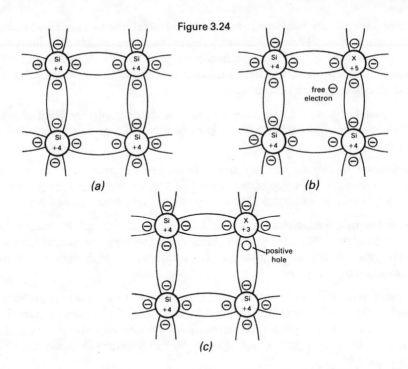

Figure 3.24

(a)

(b)

(c)

When atoms of materials, such as arsenic, which have five valence electrons are introduced (doping) into pure silicon an **n-type** semiconductor is formed. Only four of the valence electrons from the impurity atom are required to bond with four silicon atoms, figure 3.24 (b). The fifth electron is very weakly bonded and can easily become mobile. These mobile **electrons** are called **majority-charge carriers** in the **n-type** material and are obviously negatively charged.

If the material used to dope the pure silicon has only three valence electrons, as in indium, there is a **vacancy** or **positive hole** in the crystal lattice, see figure 3.24 (c). These holes can capture an electron from an adjacent silicon atom and so, in effect, the positive holes move. The **majority-charge carriers** are therefore **positive holes** in this **p-type** semiconductor.

### 3.5.7 Semiconductor diodes

#### The p-n junction diode

A p-n junction diode is made from a single crystal which is grown so that half is p-type semiconductor material while the other half is n-type.

Figure 3.25 shows the movement of charge carriers in the diode under different conditions.

Figure 3.25

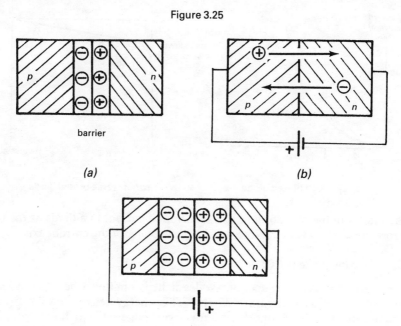

*(a)*

*(b)*

*(c)*

In figure 3.25 (a) majority carriers (electrons) from the n-type material diffuse across the junction and fill "holes" in the p-type material. The n-type material is therefore deficient in electrons at the junction and is positively charged. The p-type material is negatively charged close to the junction, because of the extra electrons. This process creates a **depletion** layer at the junction and a p.d. across the barrier thus preventing further movement of carriers.

If a sufficiently high p.d. is applied, in the direction shown in figure 3.25 (b), across the barrier, the barrier p.d. can be reduced or removed. This is called **forward-biasing** the diode. Electrons now flow from the n-type to the p-type material and holes from the p-type to the n-type.

If a p.d. is applied across the diode as in figure 3.25 (c), **reverse-biasing**, the barrier p.d. is reinforced and the diode does not conduct. In fact there is a very small current called the **leakage current** when the diode is reverse biased.

121

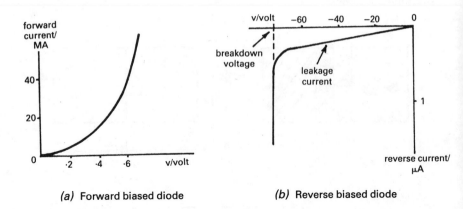

Figure 3.26

*(a)* Forward biased diode

*(b)* Reverse biased diode

The graphs in figure 3.26 show the variation of current in a diode as the p.d. across the diode is varied. Note the change in scale for the current axis.

**Light emitting diode (LED)**

In certain types of p-n junction diodes light is emitted when the diode is forward biased as in figure 3.25 (b). This energy release results from a **recombination** of electrons from the n-type material and holes from the p-type material in the depletion layer. Each recombination results in the release of a quantum of energy. The amount of energy involved can be calculated from $E = hf$, where $f$ is the frequency of the emitted light.

**Photodiode**

Photodiodes are constructed in such a way that the junction region can be exposed to light. They are used in two modes: the **photovoltaic** mode and the **photoconductive** mode.

*(a)* **Photovoltaic** mode. Each photon of light falling on the junction frees an electron to create an electron-hole pair. The electron and hole move in opposite directions and increase the p.d. across the barrier, see figure 3.25 (a). The size of this e.m.f. increases with the intensity of the light and thus the photodiode can be used as a source of electrical energy (solar cell).

*(b)* **Photoconductive** mode. If the diode is **reverse-biased** as in figure 3.25 (c) the charge carriers (electrons and holes) which are created by the incident photons, produce a current which adds to the leakage current shown in figure 3.26 (b).

122

Figure 3.27

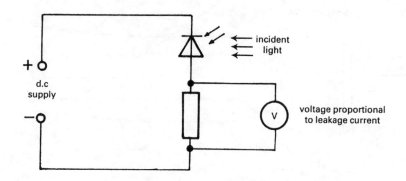

A photodiode used in the **photoconductive** mode as in figure 3.27 can be used as a **light sensor** because:

(i) the leakage current is directly proportional to the intensity of light incident on the junction;

(ii) the leakage current is independent of the reverse-biasing voltage (up to the breakdown voltage of the diode);

(iii) it responds rapidly to changes in light level.

## 3.6 RADIOACTIVITY

### 3.6.1 Nuclear Model

#### Alpha-Particle Scattering

In the experiment proposed by Rutherford and performed by Geiger and Marsden $\alpha$-particles were fired at thin gold foil. The distribution of paths of the scattered $\alpha$-particles was found by detectors which could be moved to various positions as in figure 3.28 (a).

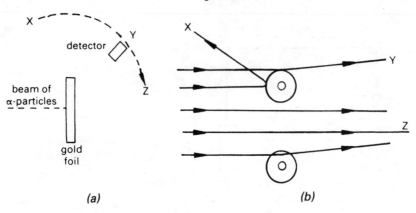

Figure 3.28

**Note:**

*(a)* Most α-particles passed straight through the foil indicating that the atom was mostly "empty" space, i.e. the mass of the atom was not uniformly distributed throughout the atom.

*(b)* About 1 in 8000 positively charged α-particles was deflected back to be detected at positions such as $X$. This gives evidence for the positively charged nature of the nucleus and for its large mass.

**The Model of the Nucleus**

The simplest model of the nucleus has the following characteristics:

1. the nucleus has a small diameter compared with the atom to which it belongs,
2. the mass of an atom is concentrated in the nucleus,
3. the nucleus contains positively charged particles (protons) and uncharged particles (neutrons),
4. the number of protons in a nucleus is unique to an element.

A **nuclide** is a nucleus of an element uniquely specified by the number of protons and neutrons and represented by the symbol $^A_Z X$, e.g. $^{238}_{92} U$ where:

1. Z is the **proton** or **atomic number** and is the number of protons in the nucleus.
2. A is the **nucleon** or **mass number** and gives the number of nucleons, i.e. protons **plus** neutrons in the nucleus. Hence $(A - Z)$ is the number of neutrons.
3. X is the chemical symbol of the element.

**Isotopes** of an element, e.g. $^{238}_{92}U$ and $^{235}_{92}U$ have the same proton number Z but different mass numbers, i.e. they have a different number of neutrons.

Symbols used for subatomic particles are proton $^1_1p$, neutron $^1_0n$, electron $^0_{-1}e$ where the superscript gives the mass number and the subscript gives the charge in multiples of the charge on one electron.

### 3.6.2 Radioactivity

An **unstable** or **radioactive** nucleus can spontaneously disintegrate with the emission of particles such as $\alpha$-particles and $\beta$-particles or $\gamma$-rays.

Properties of $\alpha$, $\beta$ particles and $\gamma$-radiation

| *Property* | $\alpha$ | $\beta$ | $\gamma$ |
|---|---|---|---|
| Nature symbol | *He* nucleus $^4_2He$ | electron $^0_{-1}e$ | photon of electromagnetic radiation |
| Charge (electronic units) | +2 | –1 | 0 |
| Mass (nucleon units) | 4 | $\dfrac{1}{1850}$ | 0 |
| Absorption | by paper sheet | several mm of Al | several cm of Pb |
| Ionising Power relative to $\alpha$-particle | 1 | $10^{-1}$ | $10^{-4}$ |
| velocity | $< 3 \times 10^6$ m s$^{-1}$ | up to about $2 \times 10^8$ m s$^{-1}$ | $3 \times 10^8$ m s$^{-1}$ |

**$\alpha$-particle emission or decay**

$$^A_ZX \rightarrow {}^{A-4}_{Z-2}Y + {}^4_2He \quad \text{e.g.} \quad {}^{226}_{88}Ra \rightarrow {}^{222}_{86}Rn + {}^4_2He$$

parent nucleus    daughter nucleus    $\alpha$-particle

Note:   1. total charge is conserved;
        2. total number of nucleons is conserved, i.e.

$$A = (A-4) + 4 \quad \text{and} \quad Z = (Z-2) + 2$$

### β-Particle Emission or Decay

$$_{Z}^{A}X \rightarrow _{Z+1}^{A}Y + _{-1}^{0}e \quad \text{e.g.} \quad _{38}^{90}Sr \rightarrow _{39}^{90}Y + _{-1}^{0}e$$

parent      daughter    β-particle
nucleus     nucleus

Note again

$$A = A + 0 \text{ and } Z = (Z + 1) + (-1)$$

Daughter nuclei formed by α or β decay are usually unstable and lose excess energy by emitting γ-radiation.

The decay of a group of radioactive nuclei is **random**, i.e. it is not possible to predict when any particular nucleus will decay. If the sample contains a large number of nuclei we can however predict a time after which half the nuclei will have decayed. This time is the half-life $T_{1/2}$ for the particular nuclide. The half-life is the same for all samples of a particular nuclide.

If a graph of the number of undecayed nuclei against time is plotted the half-life can be calculated as in figure 3.29

Figure 3.29

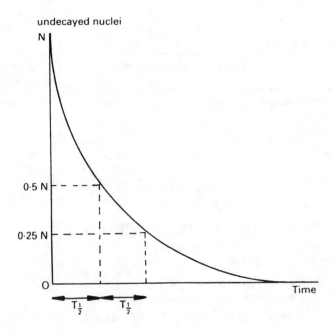

126

## Half-value thickness

In a situation which requires the use of radioactive sources how can the hazard be minimised?

Dose equivalent can be reduced by

1. increasing the distance between the source and the absorbing material, e.g. using tongs;

2. placing a shield between the source and the absorbing material. Note that the shield itself must be an absorber.

The apparatus in figure 3.30 can be used to investigate the effect of different thicknesses of shielding material, e.g. lead, on the intensity of γ-radiation reaching a Geiger Muller tube.

### Figure 3.30

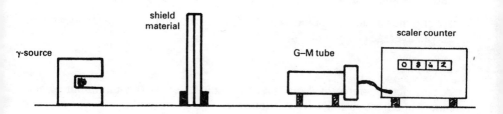

First the average background count rate is measured. A known thickness of shield material is then placed in front of the source and the average count rate measured. This count rate is then "corrected" by subtraction of the average background count rate.

If the experiment is repeated for various thicknesses of shield material a graph of the type shown in figure 3.31 can be obtained.

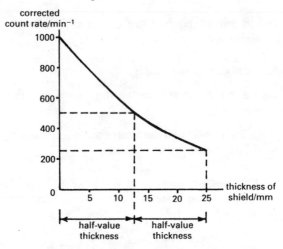

Figure 3.31

The half-value thickness of a material is that thickness of material which when placed in a beam of radiation will reduce the intensity (count rate) to half of its initial value.

Several measurements of half-value thickness should be taken from the graph and an average calculated.

*Example 3.5*

A radioactive source of γ-rays gives a count rate of 400 count/minute when placed at a fixed distance from a detector.

What is the new count rate if a lead shield of thickness 45 mm is placed between the source and the detector. The half-value thickness of lead is 15 mm for this type of radiation.

Solution:

| Thickness of shield mm | Number of half-value thicknesses | Count rate counts/minute |
|---|---|---|
| 0 | 0 | 400 |
| 15 | 1 | 200 |
| 30 | 2 | 100 |
| 45 | 3 | 50 |

The new count rate is 50 counts/minute.

128

### 3.6.3 Radiation Hazards

High energy radiation causes ionisation in human tissue and can damage body cells. In order to estimate hazards and monitor the effects of radiation the following factors must be considered:

(a) the strength or activity of the radioactive source;

(b) the amount of energy absorbed by the absorbing material;

(c) the type of radiation — α, β, γ etc.;

(d) the time span of the exposure to radiation.

How are these taken into account? First we define the following physical quantities.

(a) **Activity A** of a quantity of radioactive substance is the number of nuclei which decay per second. As radioactivity is a random process A must be the average over several measurements. The unit of activity is the becquerel, Bq. One becquerel is one decay per second.

(b) **Absorbed dose D** is the energy absorbed per kilogram of the absorbing material. The unit is the gray, Gy. Different materials subjected to the same type and energy of radiation will have different absorbed doses.

(c) **Quality factor Q**. The damage done to the absorbing material depends on the type of radiation and the energy of individual particles of the radiation (contrasted with total energy of the radiation). For example, alpha particles cause more damage than X-rays because the alpha particles produce more ionisation.

Each radiation type and energy is given a quality factor, e.g. γ-rays $Q = 1$, α-particles $Q = 20$.

(d) **Dose equivalent H**. By using the absorbed dose for each type of radiation and its corresponding quality factor we can define dose equivalent $H = DQ$. This quantity standardises the effects of different radiations being absorbed by a material. The total dose equivalent can then be calculated by summing the contributions from various radiations. The unit of dose equivalent is the Sievert, Sv.

For members of the public the dose equivalent should not be greater than 5 mSv in any year (in addition to that from background radiation) and not greater than 1 mSv in a year as an average over several years.

For workers exposed as part of their employment the upper limit is set at 50 mSv in any year.

(e) **Dose equivalent rate $\dot{H}$.** The dose equivalent rate is the dose equivalent during a certain time interval divided by that time interval, $\dot{H} = \dfrac{H}{t}$. The unit is mSv yr$^{-1}$ or mSv h$^{-1}$.

(f) **Background radiation.** The radiation always present in the environment results from various sources such as, cosmic rays, soil and rocks, the radioactivity of the human body, radon gas.

The average dose equivalent from background radiation is 2·0 mSv per year.

The use of the above quantities can be seen from the following example.

*Example 3.6*

A worker receives an absorbed dose of 20 mGy of $\gamma$-radiation and 200 $\mu$Gy of fast neutrons during his working year of 40 weeks.

(a) Assuming that $Q = 1$ for $\gamma$-rays and $Q = 10$ for fast neutrons, calculate the dose equivalent for the year.

(b) If the worker is exposed to the radiation for 20 hours during each week, what is his average dose equivalent rate?

Solution:

(a) $H = DQ$

for $\gamma$-rays $\quad H = 20 \times 10^{-3} \times 1 \quad = 20 \times 10^{-3}$ Sv

for fast neutrons $H = 200 \times 10^{-6} \times 10 = 2 \times 10^{-3}$ Sv

$\Rightarrow$ total dose equivalent $= 22$ mSv

(b) Dose equivalent rate $= \dfrac{\text{dose equivalent}}{\text{time}}$

$$= \frac{22 \times 10^{-3}}{40 \times 20} \text{ Sv h}^{-1}$$

$$= 27{\cdot}5 \times 10^{-6} \text{ Sv h}^{-1}$$

$$= 27{\cdot}5 \text{ } \mu\text{Sv h}^{-1}$$

## 3.6.4 $E = mc^2$ and Binding Energy

Einstein's relationship $E = mc^2$ is perhaps the best known in Physics. But what does it mean? Simply that mass may be regarded as another form of energy.

An object **at rest** with a "rest mass" $m_0$ has a "rest mass energy" given by

$E = m_0 c^2$ where $E$ is in J

$m_0$ is in kg

$c$ equals $3 \times 10^8$ m s$^{-1}$, the velocity of light in vacuo.

If the object acquires kinetic energy then $E$ will increase and hence its mass increases. For nuclear interactions the energy changes involved cause relatively large mass changes. For everyday experience the changes are small. For example a ball of mass 1 kg gaining 100 J of kinetic energy would have a mass increase of about $1 \times 10^{-15}$ kg.

When nucleons bind together to form a nucleus there is a decrease in potential energy (consider the analogy of a stone falling and "binding" to the Earth's surface). The decrease in potential energy is observed as a decrease in total rest mass. Conversely to split a nucleus into separate nucleons requires energy: this energy is called the **binding energy**. For the interaction

$$^{238}_{92}U \rightarrow 92\,^1_1H + 146\,^1_0n$$

The above could have been written as

$$\begin{array}{c} \text{Mass energy of} \\ ^{238}_{92}U \end{array} + \begin{array}{c} \text{Binding} \\ \text{Energy} \end{array} = \begin{array}{c} \text{Mass energy of} \\ \text{92 protons} \end{array} + \begin{array}{c} \text{Mass energy of} \\ \text{146 neutrons} \end{array}$$

or

$$\begin{array}{c} \text{Rest mass of} \\ ^{238}_{92}U \end{array} + \begin{array}{c} \text{Mass equivalent of} \\ \text{Binding Energy} \end{array} = \begin{array}{c} \text{Rest mass of} \\ \text{92 protons} \end{array} + \begin{array}{c} \text{Rest mass of} \\ \text{146 neutrons} \end{array}$$

The mass equivalent of the binding energy found from $E = mc^2$ is called the **mass defect**.

> Mass defect = Sum of masses of nucleons – Mass of nucleus

The binding energy per nucleon for a particular type of nucleus is the binding energy of that nucleus divided by the number of nucleons in it. Note a **higher** binding energy implies a **lower** potential energy and greater stability of the nucleus. The binding energy has a maximum for iron then falls to uranium as shown in figure 3.32.

Figure 3.32

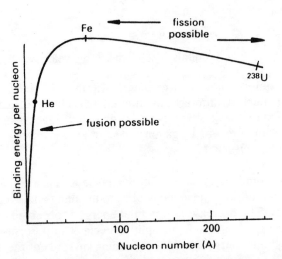

The position of iron with the maximum binding energy per nucleon indicates two ways of obtaining energy from the nucleus. The first is **fission** for nuclei heavier than iron and **fusion** for nuclei lighter than iron.

### 3.6.5 Nuclear Fission

Nuclear Fission is the splitting of heavy nuclei such as $^{235}_{92}U$ into two or more smaller nuclei accompanied by the release of energy. Fission can be **spontaneous** or **induced** by extra energy being given to the nucleus by neutrons, electrons or electromagnetic radiation.

The steps in the model of an induced nuclear fission reaction illustrated in figure 3.33 are:

Figure 3.33

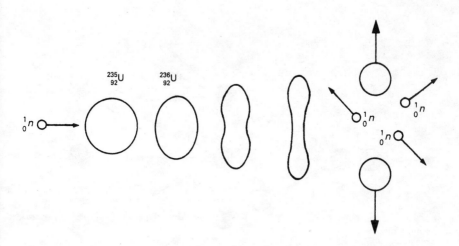

1.  A thermal or slow neutron is absorbed by a U-235 nucleus.

2.  An unstable nucleus of U-236 is formed and left in an unstable state.

3.  The vibrations of the U-236 result in a nonspherical nucleus having two centres of positive charge.

4.  The electrostatic repulsion between the two centres of positive charge cause fission to occur.

5.  The kinetic energy of the fission products accounts for most of the energy released during fission.

6.  Further fast neutrons are released during the fission. If slowed down by passing through a **moderator**, e.g. graphite, they become thermal neutrons and can cause fission in other U-235 nuclei. If the process is self-sustaining it is called a **chain reaction** as in figure 3.34.

Figure 3.34

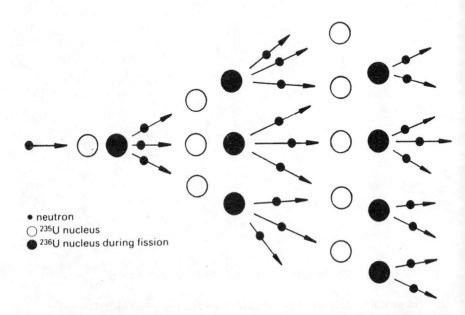

- ● neutron
- ○ 235U nucleus
- ● 236U nucleus during fission

Figure 3.32 shows that for elements with a mass number greater than that of iron the binding energy per nucleon decreases with increasing nucleon number (the potential energy increases). Hence when a heavy nucleus (with high potential energy) splits to form smaller nuclei the excess potential energy is released mainly as kinetic energy of the products. The loss of potential energy is observed as a decrease in total mass.

This can be written as

$$\begin{matrix}\text{Rest mass of nucleus}\\ \text{undergoing fission}\end{matrix} = \begin{matrix}\text{Sum of rest masses of}\\ \text{fission products}\end{matrix} + \text{Mass defect}$$

or

$$\begin{matrix}\text{Mass energy of nucleus}\\ \text{undergoing fission}\end{matrix} = \begin{matrix}\text{Total mass energy of}\\ \text{fission products}\end{matrix} + \begin{matrix}\text{Energy released}\\ \text{during fission}\end{matrix}$$

The energy released during fission is related to the mass defect by $E = m c^2$.

The following describes a typical induced nuclear fission reaction.

$$^{235}_{92}U + ^{1}_{0}n \rightarrow ^{141}_{56}Ba + ^{92}_{36}Kr + 3^{1}_{0}n + \text{energy}$$

The total rest mass of the nucleon and neutron on the left-hand side of this reaction is greater than the total rest mass on the right-hand side. The "lost mass" $m$ is used in $E = mc^2$ to calculate the energy released. This energy appears as kinetic energy of the fission products.


### 3.6.6 Nuclear Fusion

Nuclear fusion is the joining together of two light nuclei to form a larger nucleus. Figure 3.32 shows that for elements with nucleon numbers less than that of iron there is a rapid increase in binding energy per nucleon (i.e. a decrease in potential energy). Hence if two light nuclei of say $^{2}_{1}H$ combine to form a nucleus of $^{3}_{2}He$ there will be a decrease in potential energy (increase in binding energy per nucleon). This decrease in potential energy being mainly released as kinetic energy and gamma radiation. The released energy is observed as a decrease in rest mass and is related to the mass defect by $E = m c^2$. This can be written as

$$\begin{matrix} \text{Total rest mass of nuclei} \\ \text{undergoing fusion} \end{matrix} = \begin{matrix} \text{Total rest mass of} \\ \text{fusion products} \end{matrix} + \text{Mass defect}$$

or

$$\begin{matrix} \text{Mass energy of nuclei} \\ \text{undergoing fusion} \end{matrix} = \begin{matrix} \text{Total mass energy of} \\ \text{fusion products} \end{matrix} + \begin{matrix} \text{Energy released} \\ \text{during fusion} \end{matrix}$$

The following describes a typical nuclear fusion reaction.

$$^{2}_{1}H + ^{2}_{1}H \rightarrow ^{3}_{2}He + ^{1}_{0}n + \text{energy}$$

The energy released is calculated from

$$\begin{aligned}
\text{Rest mass of deuteron} &= 3 \cdot 343 \times 10^{-27} \text{ kg} \\
\text{Rest mass of helium-3} &= 5 \cdot 005 \times 10^{-27} \text{ kg} \\
\text{Rest mass of neutron} &= 1 \cdot 675 \times 10^{-27} \text{ kg} \\
\text{Total rest mass of LHS} &= 2 \times 3 \cdot 343 \times 10^{-27} \\
&= 6 \cdot 686 \times 10^{-27} \text{ kg} \\
\text{Total rest mass of RHS} &= 5 \cdot 005 \times 10^{-27} + 1 \cdot 675 \times 10^{-27} \\
&= 6 \cdot 680 \times 10^{-27} \text{ kg} \\
\text{Mass defect} &= 6 \cdot 686 \times 10^{-27} - 6 \cdot 680 \times 10^{-27} \\
&= 0 \cdot 006 \times 10^{-27} \\
\text{Energy released} &= mc^2 \\
&= 6 \times 10^{-30} \times (3 \times 10^8)^2 \\
&= 5 \cdot 4 \times 10^{-13} \text{ J}
\end{aligned}$$

135

# Chapter 4

## SIGNIFICANT FIGURES AND ERRORS

### SIGNIFICANT FIGURES

The answers to all calculations must be given to the appropriate number of significant figures.

An electric current measurement expressed as 3·62 A is given as three significant figures.

3·00 A implies a greater accuracy than a current expressed as 3·0 A (two significant figures).

*Example 4.1*

A resistor has a p.d. of 6·23 V across it when the current in it is 1·82 A. Calculate the value of the resistor.

$$R = \frac{V}{I} = \frac{6 \cdot 23}{1 \cdot 82} = 3 \cdot 42307 \; \Omega$$

Since $V$ and $I$ are given to only three significant figures, $R$ can be given to only three significant figures

$R = 3 \cdot 42 \; \Omega$.

## 4.2 ERRORS

All measurements of physical quantities may be subject to error.

There are three types of error to consider.

1. **Systematic error**. This type can result from an incorrectly calibrated scale on an instrument. For example, an ammeter which shows a value of 0·1 A when there is no current in it has a systematic error of 0·1 A. All values of current taken from this meter will probably be 0·1 A too high.

2. **Random error**. Repeated measurements of, for example the acceleration of a trolley down a ramp will produce a spread of values. This is because of many effects beyond the control of the experimenter, such as a variation in roughness of the surface of the ramp.

   **Random errors have an equal probability of giving a higher or lower reading**. Averaging a sufficient number of results therefore reduces the effect of this type of error.

3. **Reading error** indicates the accuracy to which a scale on an instrument can be read.

   A metre stick which is marked off in 1 mm divisions can be read to the nearest half-division, i.e. an error of ± 0·5 mm. Figure 4.1 illustrates this.

Figure 4.1

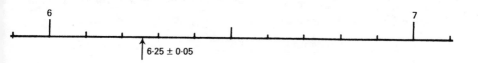

A digital meter will always have a possible error of ± 1 on the last digit. A digital voltmeter showing a value of 9·63 will have an error of ± 0·01.

This type of error can be reduced by repeated measurement and averaging the results.

Figure 4.2 shows the result of plotting the values of a measured quantity, say acceleration, from a series of identical experiments against the number of times a particular value is obtained.

Figure 4.2

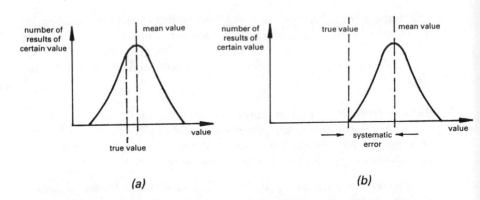

*(a)*

*(b)*

In (a) there is only random or reading error so the mean value for the quantity is close to the true value. In (b) there is a large systematic error, so the mean value is very different from the true value.

**The mean value obtained from repeated measurements is the best estimate of the true value of the quantity being measured.** Care must be taken to avoid systematic error.

### Error in the mean

If a set of $n$ measurements of the same quantity is made, the approximate random error may be calculated using

$$\text{random error} = \frac{(\text{maximum value} - \text{minimum value})}{n}$$

*Example 4.2*

Repeated measurements of $g$ give the following values in m s$^{-2}$:

9·86, 9·80, 9·79, 9·84.

What is the best value of $g$ and its error?

138

Solution:

mean value of $g = \dfrac{9 \cdot 86 + 9 \cdot 80 + 9 \cdot 79 + 9 \cdot 84}{4} = 9 \cdot 82$

random error $= \dfrac{9 \cdot 86 - 9 \cdot 79}{4} = 0 \cdot 0175 = 0 \cdot 02$

Best value of $g = 9 \cdot 82 \pm 0 \cdot 02 \text{ m s}^{-2}$

**Error in a calculation from several quantities**

This is best shown by an example.

*Example 4.3*

If a resistance is calculated from measured values of voltage and current the value of the resistance will be liable to error. The following measurements are obtained from such an experiment. Find the best estimate of the resistance and give your answer in the form —

resistance $\pm$ error.

Measurement of p.d. $= 20 \cdot 00 \pm 0 \cdot 02$ V

Measurement of current $= 2 \cdot 00 \pm 0 \cdot 02$ A

Solution:

[The $\pm 0 \cdot 02$ is the absolute error. First **calculate the percentage errors in the voltage and current.**]

p.d. $= 20 \cdot 00 \pm \dfrac{0 \cdot 02}{20 \cdot 00} \times 100 = 20 \cdot 00 \text{ V} \pm 0 \cdot 1\%$

current $= 2 \cdot 00 \text{ A} \pm \dfrac{0 \cdot 02}{2 \cdot 00} \times 100 = 2 \cdot 00 \text{ A} \pm 1\%$

[**Identify the quantity with the largest percentage error and assume this approximates to the error in the final quantity.**]

$R \doteq \dfrac{V}{I} = \dfrac{20 \cdot 00}{2 \cdot 00} = 10 \ \Omega \pm 1\% = 10 \cdot 0 \pm 0 \cdot 1 \ \Omega$

# Chapter 5

## PROBLEM SOLVING

### 5.1 PROBLEMS

You will have to gain experience in solving numerical problems. This can best be done using past examination papers for the course. Some examples of other types of problems are given below.

Note that you might find it easier to insert values for the relevant quantities in some questions and solve the problems numerically.

1.  A ball is lifted to a certain height above the ground then dropped. A second ball, with twice the mass of the first, is raised to the same height then dropped. How does the kinetic energy of the first ball compare with the kinetic energy of the second ball just before they hit the ground?

2.  A ball is dropped from a certain height and strikes the pavement. Show that the ball would have to be dropped from four times the first height to double the speed of impact of the ball with the pavement.

3.  A stone is thrown vertically into some mud. It penetrates 1 cm into the mud. What should be the speed of the stone on impact to make it penetrate 4 cm into the mud? Assume that the force of friction is constant in the mud.

4.  An open truck is moving along a frictionless surface. Blocks are dropped vertically into the truck. What happens to

    *(a)* the momentum of the truck and contents
    *(b)* the speed of the truck
    *(c)* the kinetic energy of the truck and contents?

5.  A ship is pulled at constant speed by two tugs as shown below. What is the effect on the motion of the ship if the angle X of the tow ropes is decreased? Justify your answer.

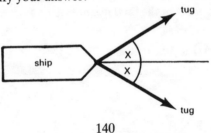

**6.** A sphere with an initial horizontal velocity leaves the edge of a bench as shown.

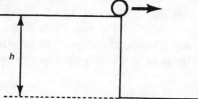

If the height of the edge of the bench is increased by a factor of four times, what is the effect on

(a) the time of flight

(b) the distance the sphere lands from the foot of the bench?

**7.** A cylinder floats upright in a container of fresh water. Describe and explain what happens when the same cylinder is placed in a container of salt water.

**8.** A bubble of gas rises from the bottom of a pool of water. Explain what happens to the volume of the bubble as it rises.

**9.** A sunken ship on the sea-bed can be raised to the surface by filling the ship with polystyrene. Explain the principles of this method.

**10.** The refractive index of light of a material depends on the frequency of light: the frequency of light does not depend on the refractive index of the material. Discuss.

**11.** Red light passes through a diffraction grating and maxima and minima of intensity are obtained on a screen. How can the distance between maxima and minima be increased using the same wavelength of light.

**12.** When a clean zinc plate is illuminated with ultraviolet light of a certain wavelength, electrons are emitted from the zinc. When the experiment is repeated using a copper plate instead of a zinc plate there are no electrons emitted. Why?

## 5.2 SOLUTIONS

1. Potential energy is given by *mgh*. The initial potential energy of the second ball is twice that of the first. When the ball falls its potential energy is converted to kinetic energy. **The kinetic energy of the second ball on reaching the ground will therefore be twice that of the first.**

2. Using the equation of motion

   $v^2 = u^2 + 2as$ and since the object falls from rest, $u = 0$.

   $\Rightarrow v^2 = 2as$ and since 2 and $a$ are constants

   $\Rightarrow v^2 \alpha s$ or $v \alpha \sqrt{s}$    $v = k\sqrt{s}$    $2v = k\sqrt{4s}$

   $\Rightarrow$ **to double the speed we need to multiply the height by a factor of four**

   **OR** by conservation of energy

   P.E. at top = K.E. at bottom : $mgh = \frac{1}{2} mv^2 : h \alpha v^2$, etc.

3. The kinetic energy, $\frac{1}{2} mv^2$ of the stone is converted to heat energy by friction. If the force of friction is assumed to be constant then the work done against friction is given by the product $Fd$ where $d$ is the stopping distance of the ball.

   $\frac{1}{2} mv^2 = Fd$ since $F$, $m$ and $\frac{1}{2}$ are constants then:

   $d \alpha v^2 : d = kv^2 : 4d = (2v)^2$ so **to increase $d$ by a factor of four we need only to double the speed**.

4. The truck has only horizontal momentum whereas the blocks have only vertical momentum. The horizontal **momentum of the truck therefore remains constant**. Since the mass of the truck and its contents increases while the momentum remains constant, **the velocity must decrease**.

   If the mass of the truck is doubled then the new speed of the truck will be half of its original value: $v^2$ will be a quarter of its original value. Hence the new kinetic energy $\frac{1}{2} mv^2$ will be less than its original value. **The kinetic energy will decrease**.

5. The easterly component of the force caused by each tug is F cos X. The total easterly component is therefore 2F cos X. As X decreases, cos X increases and hence the easterly force increases. If the frictional force remains constant the ship will accelerate.

6. Time of flight is given by time for vertical drop. $S_v = \frac{1}{2} a_v t^2$ giving $S_v = kt^2$ where $k$ is a constant. If $S_v$ is increased by a factor of four then **$t$ will be increased by a factor of two**, i.e. $4S_v = k(2t)^2$.

$S_H = u_H t$. The time of the flight is doubled therefore **the range $S_H$ is doubled**.

7. The density of salt water is greater than the density of fresh water. Hence the upwards pressure ($p = k\rho h$) and force on the bottom of the cylinder will be greater in salt water than in fresh at the same depth. The weight of the cylinder remains constant. The cylinder will remain at a certain depth when the upthrust at that depth equals the weight of the cylinder. **The cylinder will have less of its length submerged in salt water**.

8. The pressure caused by the liquid on the gas bubble will decrease as the bubble rises ($p = \rho g h$). From the gas law $pV = $ constant, as the pressure decreases **the volume increases**.

9. When the ship is on the sea-bed the weight of the ship, including the water inside, must be greater than the upthrust. Polystyrene is less dense than water so when the ship is filled with polystyrene its new weight is less than the upthrust and ship rises to the surface.

10. The refractive index of a material depends on the frequency of the light passing through it. This allows the formation of spectra using a prism. The frequency of a wave from a source only depends on the source and not on the material it travels in.

11. The relationship to use is $d \sin \theta = n\lambda$ or $\sin \theta = \dfrac{n\lambda}{d}$. We want to increase $\theta$ and hence increase $\sin \theta$, see Figure 3.4. This can be done by decreasing $d$, the line spacing of the grating, i.e. using **a grating with a greater number of lines per metre**. Also since $x = D \sin \theta$ we can **increase D, the distance between the grating and the screen**.

12. If the ultraviolet light causes photoelectric emission from the zinc the energy of the photons must be greater than the work function of the zinc. The energy of the photons of this radiation must be less than the work function of the copper if no photoelectric emission takes place.

Printed in Great Britain by Bell and Bain Ltd., Glasgow